STILL ANOTHER NORTHWOODS READER

Copyright 1989
by Cully Gage
and
Avery Color Studios
Marquette, Michigan 49855

Written by Cully Gage
Illustrated by Andrew Amor
Cover Photo by Hoyt Avery

Library of Congress Card No. 89-80866
ISBN # 0-932212-61-1
First Edition—October 1989
Reprinted—1990, 1991, 1995

Published by
Avery Color Studios
Marquette, Michigan 49855

To Cathy

TABLE OF CONTENTS

The Inheritance.. 9

Thanksgiving, 1913 19

Save The Last Dance For Me.................................. 26

Yarn for Deer Camp 33

The Reclamation of Scotty McGee 38

The U.P. Dialect.. 47

The Peaceful Little Village of Tioga 58

Killing Three Birds With One Cheese 64

Smoke Rings 70

The Sad Side 76

Laughing Our Way Through Winter 84

The Old Logging Days 89

Teaching My Bride To Fish 98

The Lie.. 105

Going Back to the U.P....................................... 113

Not Yet 118

One Day in May, 1915.. 134

Postscript 142

FOREWORD

One of my joys when growing up in the little forest village of Tioga during the early years of this century was listening to our old men telling tales. They were first-class storytellers, skillful at building suspense at the crucial moments by lighting and relighting their corncob pipes, or just pretending to have lost their train of thought. We had no TV, radio or movies in Tioga and few books or magazines, so storytelling was about the only entertainment our people had out of bed except fishing and hunting. In these Northwoods Readers I have tried to continue the tradition, while also portraying the sort of life we led back then and the kind of people who lived it.

Cully Gage
3821 W. Milham
Portage, MI 49002

THE INHERITANCE

In my other Northwoods Readers I've told several tales about Eino, the swarthy little Finn and Emil, the big blonde Norwegian who lived happily in Tioga long ago. Here's another one about those two old bachelors who lived in houses next to each other up by the old mine.

First of all, I must tell you about how they managed to live so well despite being seventy years of age and long unemployed. Both had little pensions of $30 a month from the mining company for which they'd worked for many years. That may not seem like very much now, but then a dollar was worth twenty times what it goes for today. Besides, they didn't need much biting money because they shot a lot of deer in season and out, caught trout and pike all summer, and they had a common garden that produced all the potatoes, cabbage and rutabagas they needed. Emil had a chicken yard and coop behind his house, while Eino had a cow and cowbarn, so they had all the milk and eggs and butter they needed. Emil did the canning of meat, apples, and berries; Eino did the baking. No, they may not have had much but they had enough, and they shared everything together. Neither had a care in the world. Life was very, very good.

9

Or it was until one day Emil got a letter from Norway. "It's a registered letter," Annie, our postmistress told me when she asked me to notify Emil, "and he has to sign for it up here in person. Tell him it looks important."

I heard Eino and Emil arguing long before I got to their houses to find the two old buggers sitting on empty nail kegs on Eino's porch, playing checkers on a third keg between them. "Yump!" shouted Emil, "Yump, you dumb Finn. Why don't you yump?"

"No," said Eino in his quiet voice. "I no jump. I no so dumb. If I jump then you jump two, three times. No!"

Finally I got their attention and told Emil about the registered letter waiting for him up at the post office. "Annie says it's from Norway and you should come get it right away."

The old Norwegian scratched his head. "Who from?" he said. "My father, mother they die long ago. No brother. One sister I write to three time and never hear back. Maybe she dead too." He sure was puzzled.

So was my father that afternoon when Emil and Eino came to him, Emil waving the letter and explaining and asking, all in a confused jumble that Dad couldn't make head or tail of. "You sign paper for me, Doctor, eh? Paper saying me Emil Olsen. I got no pastor for say it. No Norwegian church here. Swede Lutheran but I don't go. Hell with Swedes! Maybe I get money, eh?" He opened the letter and showed it to my father.

Dad shook his head. "Emil, I can't read Norwegian and I can't make any sense about what you're trying to tell me. I suggest you take your letter over to Leif Backe's house in Halfway and have him translate it into English, then bring it back and I'll see if I can help you."

After the two men left, Dad shook his head. "Lord, the problems our people bring me!" he muttered. It was true. Since many of our villagers were first generation immigrants and were literate only in their own languages, Finnish, French and others, whenever they were faced with any kind of legal document they came to my father for advice because he was educated and because they trusted him completely. He had examined contracts for pulpwood, notices of jury duty, sales agreements, oh a lot of other things. Not that he ever played lawyer, he always referred people to Tim Clancy in Ishpeming if the problem needed more than just explaining.

This is the letter's translation that Emil and Eino brought back to Dad the next day:

> "As executors of the estate of Knud Olsen, deceased May 2, 1915, we are seeking to locate one Emil Olsen, nephew of said Knud Olsen. According to our information, he never married nor had children and there seem to be only two possible beneficiaries, a niece and nephew, Aud Olsen, now deceased, of Tronheim, Norway, and Emil

Olsen who emigrated to the United States of America about the year 1870. A letter found in the effects of Aud Olsen, gives the address of said Emil Olsen as being of Tioga, Michigan, U.S.A., and it is to that address this letter is being sent.

In order to be certain that you are indeed Knud Olsen's nephew and beneficiary, it is necessary that you provide the following: 1. The names of your father and mother; 2. The date and place of your birth; 3. Statements from your pastor and/or mayor that you are said Emil Olsen. Upon receipt of the above information, providing that it is satisfactory, we shall send you the bank draft of your legacy."

After reading the translation Dad said, "Well, Emil, it looks like you're coming into some money. I'll write you out a statement saying that you exist. We don't have a mayor but I'm township supervisor and that should be good enough. I'll write it on official stationery and stamp it with the township seal so it'll look official." This is what Dad wrote:

"I hereby certify that Emil Olsen, formerly of Trondheim, Norway, has been a citizen of this village of Tioga, Michigan for at least twenty years. I know him well both as an employee and as a medical patient."

He then signed his name and embossed the letter with the Township seal. (I remember that embosser very well. Working like a stapler, I'd stamp out a lot of circles from store paper when Dad was on his house calls, then cut them out to serve as play money for our poker games up in the hayloft. Yes, even at the age of ten we boys had already learned not to try to fill an inside straight.)

So Emil mailed his letter with the enclosure to Norway and nothing much happened for two months. Meanwhile, he and Eino lived their good life getting ready for win-ter. They cut ferns and bracken and hauled many loads of leaves to the cow barn for bedding; they made wood, lots of it, enough to last till spring. They smoked thirty pike they'd caught in Lake Tioga and hung them from the rafters of Eino's summer kitchen. Potatoes and rutabagas were dug and stored in the cellars. Eino made a big jar of sauerkraut. Then they went hunting to get venison for canning when the autumn approached snow time. Every bit of it was fun, more fun than work because of the companionship felt by the two old friends. Life was very, very good.

Oh, there were a few times when Emil wished the money, if any, would come. "Maybe I get enough raha to buy a horse and wagon," said Emil when the two old men got tired of hauling the maple saplings they'd cut on Keystone Hill. And there were times when they wished they could have a drink from the bottle of whiskey they were saving for New Year's Day. But, for the most part, they just forgot about the inheritance. Let the winter come. They were ready for it. It's a good feeling that few people from Down Below can appreciate.

Then the letter came. In it was a bank draft for 35,000 kroner. About five thousand dollars. A fortune! Emil Olsen was a rich man.

He was also a very troubled man. "Now what I do?" he asked my father. "Kroner no good this country." Dad told him to take the bank draft to the Miner's National Bank in Ishpeming where for a fee they would cash it into dollars, and then to establish a checking account and a savings account. When Emil didn't know what they were, Dad tried to explain but it was obvious that the old Norwegian didn't understand.

Emil didn't sleep much that night because he kept fingering that letter under his pillow to make sure it was there. During breakfast with Eino the next morning he asked, "Eino, you got any money? I got dollar fifty, not enough to go Ishpeming on train. I pay you back. You come with me, eh?"

Eino went down to his cellar and came back with a ten dollar bill from the graveyard money he'd saved long ago. "O.K., Emil. Here enough pay round trip maybe. But you pay back. Coffin money." A lot of our old folks in Tioga had some anxiety about a proper burial. They didn't want to be shoveled naked into the cold ground. Unlike his friend, Eino had always been a lookaheader.

Neither of them had been on a train for many years so they enjoyed the ride, but when they got to Ishpeming they were lost. Finally Emil asked a passer-by where to get to Miner's Bank and was told to find the Indian statue horse trough and go north across the street. That was easy but it was a good thing Eino was there because Emil couldn't read the big sign, being illiterate in English even after many years.

When the big Norwegian presented the letter and bank draft to the teller she called the manager who asked if he wanted to deposit it in a checking or savings account. "No," said Emil. "Cash. I keep all money myself, yah." The manager told him that was unwise, that he might be robbed or lose it, that a bank account was as good as gold, but Emil was stubborn. He'd heard that banks sometimes failed. "Give money," he said, "twenty dollar bills, yah."

Now five thousand dollars in twenty dollar bills made up quite a packet and to keep enough of them for other customers the teller had to include five one hundred dollar bills and twenty fifty dollar ones. One of the latter was kept by the bank to cover the costs of the currency exchange but all the rest were counted out and put in a canvas bag labeled with the bank's name. To make sure he wasn't being cheated, Emil made the poor teller count them a second time. "Eino, you watch and count too," he whispered hoarsely. Finally they left the bank, Emil looking pregnant with the money bag under his sweater. They still had two hours to spend before the next train home.

Robbers? The thought had never come to Emil before but every man he met on the streets of Ishpeming looked as though he might be one.

12

The money sack kept trying to slip out of the front of his sweater. He had to buy a belt to keep it in place, though like most of the men in the U.P. he'd never worn one. They held up their heavy pants with suspenders, usually red ones. He needed new suspenders too; those he wore were linked to the fasteners with haywire. But that meant he'd have to open the bag to get money and he sure didn't want to do that on the street, not with all those suspicious characters coming by. Often looking behind to see if they were being followed, they made their way to Voelker's Saloon and there Emil stationed Eino to watch for robbers while he went around the back to open the money sack. Then, giving one twenty dollar bill to Eino, and keeping another in his pocket they went to Bradstad's department store where he bought a belt for fifty cents and two pairs of scarlet suspenders, one for himself and the other for Eino. The belt worked fine! He still bulged in front but the money was secure, so the two old men returned to the saloon. "We buy only two beers, Eino," Emil said. "No get drunk till we get back to Tioga." Riding on the train later he told Eino how once when he'd worked in the woods all winter up by Big Bay he'd come out with over two hundred dollars pay only to get drunk and find himself the next day without a penny of it. That wasn't going to happen this time, no sir.

When the train butcher (I don't know why they called them that but they did) rolled his cart down the aisle between the red plush covered seats monotonously chanting, "Candees, seegars, oranges, sanwiches, bananays," Emil bought two oranges, two bananas and two cigars. When you're rich you can live it up! It had been many years since either of the two old men had tasted such fruit or smoked anything but Peerless in their black corncob pipes.

They were still smoking their cigars when they got off the train at Tioga's station. "Seegars, eh, Emil?" said Francoise Vervaile when he saw them. "Got lots of raha now, I see, yes." You borrow me one dollaire for beer, maybe, for celebrate?" Unwisely Emil gave him the money. How had the village known so soon about his inheritance? Of course, everybody in Tioga always knew everything that happened to anybody and immediately. Still it was a bit unsettling. Emil didn't like the way Francoise looked at his bulging sweater either. Not that he'd ever stolen anything; no one in Tioga ever stole because everybody would know but just the same, he'd better find a good hiding place for the money. Worry wrinkles crept across the old Norwegian's forehead.

After a supper of venison stew left over from the night before, Emil went back to his house to think, an activity to which he was unaccustomed. Pulling down the window shades, he spread out all the money on the table, tried to count it to make sure, but soon gave up. Too much! Somehow he would have to find a place to hide it, but where? Should he divide it? Made no sense to have it all in the same place so someone could steal it all at once. What would he put it in? Jars? He didn't have enough empty ones. They were all full of fruit and meat. Maybe Eino would have some or he could buy some. Yah, he could buy all the jars he wanted now. Should he bury them in the garden or in the cellar or in Eino's cowbarn? Emil's head ached from all the thinking. Finally he put the money in the canvas sack, tucked it under his pillow, and went to bed, but that was too lumpy so he moved it to the bottom of the blankets. No, someone could come in and lift them and take the raha without his even waking up. Finally he put the sack between his legs at the crotch and went to sleep, a very restless sleep.

In the morning the bag was still there when it was time to go over to Eino's house for breakfast of blueberry pancakes with maple syrup, blueberries they'd picked together in July month, and the syrup they'd boiled down in April. That had been fun. Now he could buy them without any of the work though it really wasn't work. The coffee was weak because they'd had to be careful. He'd go up to Flynn's store and buy a whole pailful and they'd have coffee so strong that it would leave a fuzz on the tongue. Now he could have anything he wanted. Lots of raha, now! He patted the money sack he'd brought along, not wanting to leave it in his own cabin even for a moment.

"Eino," he said, as they smoked their corncob pipes afterward, "You my best friend. I got too much raha now. I give you half."

"No," Eino replied. "That your raha, Emil. I don't want. I got enough for me to make it through win-ter. What I need raha for?" That set off a long argument, another enjoyable one, but Eino could not be persuaded. "You always dumb Finn," Emil roared, "I give you free and you no take. You crazy!"

Having decided to put his money into jars and to hide them somewhere, Emil and Eino went up to Flynn's store to buy them, but that presented another problem. Emil didn't want to carry the money sack up there and he didn't want to leave it in his unlocked house. Back then in Tioga no one ever locked his house lest he insult his neighbors. Indeed neither the front nor the back door even had a lock. Finally Emil put on his old packsack with the money bag in it, after taking out two twenty dollar bills for his pocket, and up the hill street they went. The news of his inheritance had preceded them, for every person they met had to stop to congratulate Emil on his good fortune. "How much you get Emil? I hear you millionaire now, eh?" "You-sta go buy Flynn's store, Emil?" "Want to buy horse and wagon, Emil, for carry groceries?" They were genuinely happy for him but they also wanted to know if he'd gotten "stuck up," now that he was rich. That's the worst thing you can be called in the U.P. Any stranger who moved to our village was immediately and carefully scrutinized for any sign of condescension, and if it were there even in the slightest degree he was ostracized. Each of us was as good as anyone else, not better. Emil passed the testing. "Yah, I get a little money from mine uncle but no so much," he lied.

Even Mr. Flynn had heard the news. "Mr. Olsen," he said, rubbing his hands unctuously, "Instead of climbing the hill, I can send my delivery man by your house each day if you want something. You can

14

charge it and pay once a month." That was the first time anyone had called him Mister and Emil kind of liked that, so besides the Mason jars he also bought a whole ham and a can of peaches to stash in the packsack atop the money bag. "We going eat high on hog, now, Eino," he said. "Anything you want, Eino?" Eino said no.

While at the store Sulu Kangas looked surprised to see Emil buying the jars. "Why you can now, Emil? All berries gone and apples too." Emil told him he'd just shot another deer for the winter and had to put it up. Nevertheless, he knew that everyone in town would hear about it and think that he was going to hide his money in the jars. Things were sure getting complicated and that damned money was making a liar out of him.

As they boiled potatoes and fried a slice of the ham for dinner, Emil asked Eino for ideas about where to hide the money. It was a-worrying him, he said. He just couldn't be lugging that money bag everywhere all the time.

Eino wasn't much help. Every suggestion he made was rejected for one reason or another. Oh, how they argued. Finally Emil asked, "Where you hide graveyard money? Maybe I hide same place." Eino told him he kept it in his mattress. "Oh, for dumb!" Emil shouted. "Mattress first place robber look." So it went on and on.

All the rest of the month was miserable because Emil wouldn't leave his house, although he'd bought padlocks and hasps for both doors and hid the bag under the flooring of his cellar. That didn't allay his anxiety much because he always kept tearing it up to see if it was still there even if he'd only gone over to Eino's house. When Eino told him he was going nuts about that money and should forget it, Emil put his fears to a test by digging three holes in the garden, then replacing the earth and smoothing it down. The next morning it was evident that someone had been there. "Nah," said Eino when he looked. "That's no robber been there; that's a skunk been hunting grubs and worms. They always go for fresh holes." But Emil wasn't convinced. "There robbers here," he said.

No, it wasn't much fun, that money business. Eino began to go to Higley's saloon for a beer or two alone and to other places too. When deer season came, Eino had to hunt by himself and deeply resented having to lug the buck home without help. "Why hunt?" Emil said. "I buy you steaks, pork, maybe even chickens. I got lotsa money."

"Damn your raha," Eino replied. "Deer meat better, not so fat, I like walking woods too. You going money nuts, Emil." The fine fellowship was disappearing. There was anger between them although unspoken. Rarely did they play checkers together after Emil insisted they do it only at his house. Sometimes a day or two would go by without even a meal together. It was wrong, all wrong. Both were lonely and unhappy, and even their arguments were only half-hearted when they did occur.

One of them wasn't. It occurred when Eino insisted that Emil go to Ishpeming and put the money in the bank so he wouldn't have to worry about being robbed all the time. He could get out the money any time he wanted. Made no sense to keep it all in the house. Keep a hundred dollars only for spending, then go get more when he needed it. The old Norwegian grew purple with fury. "No!" he roared. "I no give bank my money. Banks go bad and I lose everything. No! No! No!" Though they argued long and hard Emil wouldn't give in. There's nothing as stubborn as a Norwegian - except perhaps a Swede.

"Then spend it and get rid of it," Eino advised. "that money got you and me in jailhouse. Spend it!"

Well, that was an idea. Emil had come to realize what a curse all that money was. It was spoiling the fine life he and Eino had lived together for so many years. He was tired of worrying day and night. Get rid of it. Yah, that made sense.

So Emil and Eino went on a spending spree the likes of which Tioga had never known. At first it was easy. They bought a case of whiskey and a keg of beer at Higley's but soon got tired of drinking it by themselves. More fun drinking at the saloon. Then they bought new mackinaws, sweaters, long underwear, many socks, boots, mittens, always getting the best but hating throwing out their old ones. Five pails of Peerless tobacco they purchased and six fancy briar pipes which bit their tongues so much they went back to the old blackened corncobs that they'd smoked for years. They got new jackknives but put them away because their old ones felt better. The new axe and crosscut saw weren't any better. A box of canned soup, a big tub of lard, a big bag of Pillsbury flour cluttered Emil's kitchen. Two slabs of bacon hung in Eino's shed though they still had half a one left from before. Emil bought a huge box of chocolates that they didn't even open. The maple sugar they'd boiled down in April was sweeter. One evening, they counted the money Emil had left and were appalled to find that it still totalled four thousand dollars.

"We got to buy big stuff," Emil said. "We never get rid of money this way. What we buy, Eino?" The old Finn gave it a lot of thought.

"How about horse and wagon and sleigh for carry wood and hay?" he suggested.

"Yah, yah, that's good," Emil answered. "And then we hire someone build horsebarn with hay loft and bins for oats and bran for cow and bags corn for chickens." He was enthusiastic again, Eino thought, more like old Emil.

So they hired John Untilla, Mullu's father, to build the barn and when it was finished they got a young horse and wagon and sleigh from Fred Hamel. For paying cash, Hamel threw in two tons of hay and five bags of oats too. They only hitched up the horse once before deep snows came, drove it down to Lake Tioga and back, and then put it up for the winter. That gave them more chores to do with feeding, throwing down hay from the loft, and shoveling manure but it would be good to have a horse in the spring when they could go way up the river fishing trout.

They counted the money again. Finding that there were still more than three thousand dollars left they were depressed. At night they pored over the Montgomery Ward catalog, even the ladies underwear section, but found nothing they wanted. One afternoon they went on the train again to Ishpeming, visiting all the stores but the only thing they bought were two big banana splits at the Chocolate Shoppe and two beers at Voelker's saloon. It sure was hard to get rid of raha!

Remembering they'd often wished for a boat they could put on Lake Tioga to fish for northerns, they offered Reino Kangas one hundred dollars for his. No, he said, I sell you boat for twenty dollars, that's all it's worth. Our people in Tioga were too honest. So they had a boat that they'd pick up next spring season after breakup.

Eino suggested buying land, maybe two forties of spruce and balsam, but Emil demurred. "When all money gone, how we pay taxes?" he asked. Eino agreed.

One of the good things that came from all this frustrated spending was that Emil had lost his fear of being robbed. Indeed, sometimes he wished someone would rob him. He tore the locks off his house and left the money bag invitingly on the kitchen table, but of course no one took it. No, the damned money bag was still there and so was the compulsion to get rid of it. It was evil. It had almost ruined their friendship and might again. "Dig a hole and drop it through ice in the lake," said Eino one day but Emil had a better idea. "No, I give it away. I give to poor."

That too wasn't easy. First of all, there weren't many of us in Tioga that by our standards could be called really poor. Though they often had little biting money, they had warm cabins and plenty of stuff in the basement they'd canned along with the potatoes they had dug. They also were very proud as the two old men found out when they tried to give them money. Katy Flanagan chased them halfway down the street with her broom when they tried to put a twenty dollar bill in her hand, despite the fact that she had four children and a long-gone husband. Others too refused to take any money and showed clearly their feelings of being insulted. In fact, the only one who accepted any was Pete Ramos who immediately headed for Higley's saloon to spend it.

The next thought that hit them was to throw a helluva party for the whole town on Midsummer's Day in June with pasties, beer and red pop for all. They'd hire an accordion band from Ishpeming for dancing and entertainment. But Tioga had no place big enough to hold nine hundred people. Where would they get the tables and benches? OK, they'd have a picnic down at the beach at Lake Tioga. Exploring the possibility, Emil and Eino went to Ishpeming's two bakeries. "A thousand pasties? You crazy?" was the response they got. Then they thought of making a long trench by the lake, filling it with charcoal and baking the world's largest pasty. How many jugs ketchup? How many jars pickles? In the end, the logistics were obviously beyond them. No, that wouldn't work.

Desperate, they came to my father for advice. He heard them out. "You mean you want to give away two or three thousand dollars? You sure?" Yes, they answered. That damned money was wrecking their lives. They didn't need it or want it. "Then give it to the churches," Dad said. "And to the library which hasn't been able to purchase a new book for twenty years."

"That good idea!" said Emil, and Eino agreed. "But I no give any Norwegian raha to Swede Lutheran church. Mine uncle Knud, he turn in grave. Catholic church, OK; Finn Lutheran, Methodist OK; yah, even Holy Roller church back Finntown OK. Library, OK too. Yah, good idea!"

So it was done. Keeping only two one hundred dollar bills for their mattresses, they divided the rest of the money five ways and distributed it to the astounded recipients. How the tongues of Tioga waggled! Father Hassell preached a sermon in their praise; so did the other pastors. The Library Board gave them a citation. They were heros in the town, though privately everyone thought they'd gone nutty in their old age.

Finally the money was all gone. Emil and Eino built a bonfire in their backyard and burned the money sack while passing a bottle of whiskey back and forth. Then they resumed their lives as they had led them long before, as though nothing had happened. A good life, yah! Two good friends together.

But on Midsummer Day when I was up at the post office Annie asked me to tell Emil that his pension check had come and another letter too. The other letter was from the lawyer in Norway. "Dear Mr. Olsen," it said, "We have discovered further assets of your late uncle and are therefore enclosing a bank draft for 15,000 kroner to conclude the settlement of his estate."

THANKSGIVING 1913

Clomp Clomp - Plop Plop; Clomp Clomp - Plop Plop. That was the familiar sound made by the hooves of old Maude as Mr. Marchand drove the horse up our hill street every morning and evening bringing the mail bags to the post office. And that was the way our days went by in the little sleepy village of Tioga in the early days of this century. Like Maude, time never galloped; it just plodded along.

Perhaps that was why we made such a big thing of our holidays. We needed something to anticipate and something to remember. December brought Christmas, January, New Years Day. With February came Valentine's Day, followed by St. Patrick's Day in March when our Irish fourth grade teacher, Miss Feeley, told us about the Kings of Ireland and pinned bits of green ribbon on us. Then came Easter, May Day, and in June Midsummer Day, the latter celebrated mainly by the Finns and Scandihoovians. The Fourth of July was one of the best ones with parades and fireworks, but August and September were barren months. Labor Day had not yet been invented. October's highlight was, of course, Halloween with dirty tricks (but no treats), and the dumping of outhouses. Finally, came Thanksgiving.

Thanksgiving in the forest village of Tioga took up most of a week. In school we always had a program about the Pilgrims which our friends and parents always attended. One year, as I recall, I was chosen to be John Alden in a skit about the Courtship of Miles Standish, a role I sure hated because I wanted to be one of the Indians. When the time came to perform I was so petrified being up there on the stage I forgot my lines and stammered miserably as I proposed for the shy Miles that Priscilla (Elsie Hebert) should marry him. "Why don't you speak for yourself, John?" Priscilla asked coyly and the audience broke out in great gales of laughter. But the show went on. The Indians and Pilgrims gnawed on the corn we'd colored yellow and munched brown paper drumsticks before we closed by singing "Over the River and Through the Woods."

Not many of the people in Tioga had ever eaten a turkey or even viewed one, though my own family always did on that important feast day. Nevertheless, they fed well on what they had, perhaps an old rooster from the chicken yard or a couple of ducks shot earlier and frozen in the back shed, or perhaps only a choked rabbit that had been snared in Goochie Swamp. But Thanksgiving meant having all you wanted to eat for once - even second helpings. It was also a day of thanks, thanks that we had survived, thanks that we had escaped the calamities that happened to others in our town. With the thanks, too, there was always a little prayer - that we'd be able to make it through the win-ter. (In Tioga, we never said winter. We always put a little pause between the syllables - as we did in saying hun-ting. The U.P. has a brogue all its own.)

No one looked forward to Thanksgiving as much as did my father, the village doctor. Dad really loved to eat - perhaps because he had almost starved when putting himself through medical school. Why he never got fat, having three big meals each day, I do not know for he stuffed himself at each one. Two of those meals always included pie with a chunk of sharp cheddar cheese. Dad liked any kind of pie but his favorite was venison mince meat pie. That mince pie was always the high point of our Thanksgiving feast. Oh, the turkey was fine, the mashed potatoes and rutabagas O.K., the oysters on the half shell very good, but it was that venison mince pie that was the zenith of the whole meal. Only that brought the compliment of compliments: "You have acquired merit, Madam!" Woe to any patient that came to the door when Dad was eating his pie.

I suspect that my Mother's anticipation of Thanksgiving was not that great. She had to do the cooking, set the table with fine linen and the fluted Haviland dishes, then afterward cope with a mountain of pots, dishes and pans. Nor did she particularly care for mince pie. This I could not understand when I was a boy for, like my father, I loved it beyond measure. Indeed, it wasn't until years later, just after I was married, when I raved about my mother's marvellous mince pie (and had shot my deer for the venison) that I understood. My new bride wrote my mother for the recipe and here it is:

20

4 pounds of venison; 2 pounds beef suet; five pounds diced apples; one pound dried figs; one pound pitted dates; four pounds golden raisins; four pounds dried currants; one cup candied citron; one cup candied orange peel; one cup candied lemon peel; eight cups beef broth; four cups boiled cider; two cups apple brandy; two cups dark rum; two cups molasses; four cups light brown sugar; two cups currant jelly; four teaspoons salt; four teaspoons ground cinnamon; two teaspoons ground nutmeg; one teaspoon ground cloves; one teaspoon mace.

Brown venison (half-inch slices) on both sides in frying pan then transfer to large pot, cover with two inches of water and cook over low heat for three hours. Cool, then dice meat finely. Also chop up apples, figs and dates and add to kettle. Also the suet. Chop up the citron, orange peel and lemon peel and stir thoroughly into beef broth, cider, brandy, molasses and rum, adding salt and spices. Simmer for two hours uncovered until thickened then can in sterilized jars. This makes eight quarts, enough for eight pies.

My lovely new bride took one look at the recipe, snorted, and bought a jar of mincemeat at the corner grocery, telling me in no uncertain terms that she would never be the saint my mother was.

It was a fine U.P. day, that Thanksgiving of 1913. New snow had fallen overnight; the sky was very blue and there was a lot of cold sunshine. Fine day for a feast! But suddenly at breakfast my mother dropped the bomb. "John," she said to my father, "what kind of pie would you like to have for dinner?"

"He gave her an incredulous look. "Why venison mincemeat pie, of course. What else?"

"I'm sorry, John," my mother replied. "All the mincemeat is gone. I used the last jar of it to make a pie that you could take to deer camp, remember? I was sure that you'd get a deer as you always do and had planned to make new mincemeat when you brought it home. But you didn't."

Dad was stunned. "No mince pie? No venison mincemeat pie on Thanksgiving?" He was outraged.

"No," Mother said quietly. "I canned sixteen quart jars of it last year but it's all gone. You can have blueberry pie, apple pie, pumpkin pie, wild blackberry pie, and I even have a quart of the sugarplum-rhubarb that you always like..."

Dad got up from the table. "No mince pie? Lord, if I'd known that I would have shot one of those does. Thanksgiving and no mince pie! No, I don't want any other kind of pie." He stalked out of the house biting his lower lip as he always did when furious.

By this time it was almost eight o'clock and time to start doing my chores, but as I passed through the kitchen Mother stopped me.

"Cully," she said, "I'd appreciate it if you'd go down to the cellar and bring up jars of pumpkin and cranberry sauce that are on the left hanging shelf. Remember when we picked them in the bog last September before the first frost came?"

Yes, I remembered those cranberries. Those little red and white globules were fun to pick out of the gray sphagnum moss. Unlike blueberries or wild raspberries, they filled up a pail in a hurry. After she thanked me Mother asked for some more help. "Cully, please take these tweezers and pluck the pinfeathers out of the turkey. I'm pressed for time even though we won't be having dinner until two o'clock. That big turkey will take five hours roasting, I'm sure. Meanwhile, I'll make your father a pumpkin pie. Once it's before him, I don't think he'll be able to resist it." Taking a big scoop of flour from the big bin of the kitchen cabinet, she sifted it on the tin-covered counter top.

Plucking those damned pinfeathers wasn't much fun. Plain tedious, it was, and I felt relieved when Mother took the tweezers from me to finish the job. "Now, Cully, remember to keep the woodbox filled and take the horse a sugar lump and put some molasses in the cow's bran pail before pouring in the hot water from the reservoir on the range. Oh yes, and put out a chunk of suet for the whiskey jacks, the Canadian Jays. It's Thanksgiving Day for them too. Oh Cully, you're a fine helper. Don't know what I'd do without you."

So I did my chores, throwing down fresh hay for the horse and cow through the holes in the loft, putting down new straw in their stalls and giving old Billy not only the sugar lump but an extra scoop of oats. Then I took scratch feed to the chickens in the coop behind my father's hospital. There were only three brown eggs that day from our little flock of Rhode Island Reds. They never laid very well once the snows came. I brought in some new firewood and swept the front porch.

By noon I was finished and the wonderful warm smells of the kitchen sure set me to hungering. Famished, I begged Mother for a cookie but she wouldn't let me have one. "No, Cully," she said, "You'll just have to save your appetite for the turkey and trimmings. Go out and play for an hour or two."

Knowing that my friends would be eating their own dinners at that time I decided instead to go up to see my friend Pete Halfshoes, our resident full-blooded Ojibway Indian. Dad said he was older than my Grampa Gage but he sure didn't look it. His long hair was jet black and there wasn't a wrinkle on his coppery brown face. I sure liked Pete Halfshoes. He'd served in the regular United States army, had fought in the Spanish-American War and had been an Indian scout in the expeditions against the Apaches. Walking with him in the woods was a revelation. He knew every animal track and forest sound and smell. Pete had a curious way of walking in the woods that I tried to imitate but couldn't, seeming to walk on his toes rather than on the balls of his feet. He didn't walk; he glided silently. But he liked me, I think, though, of course, he never said so. Pete never talked much.

22

When I got to his house, Pete Halfshoes greeted me as always by holding up the flat of his hand to which I responded in the same way. He was having his Thanksgiving dinner, eating pork and beans out of a can with a spoon. Nothing else was on the table but a cup of tea, a piece of korpua, and a handful of dried berries in a saucer. Thinking of the huge banquet that awaited me at home I was so upset I almost cried. It wasn't fair! It wasn't fair! When Pete broke off a piece of his one korpua and handed it to me I could hardly swallow it. This old Indian was sharing his meager food with me as had his ancestors with the Pilgrims on that first Thanksgiving Day. I left hurriedly. It wasn't fair!

How vividly I recall that Thanksgiving dinner of 1913. With the big brown turkey before him there was Dad at the west end of the long oval table sharpening the carving knife with the round file. Mother was opposite him pouring her tea from the gleaming silver teapot. Across from me was my little brother Joe, aged three, banging his silver cup on the highchair. Dorothy, then only one year old, was sleeping in her crib behind my mother and between the box stove and Aunt Rebecca's sea shell cabinet. On the south wall of the dining room hung the huge wolf skin while above the door the deer head with its huge antlers presided. The table with many dishes on the white linen tablecloth was full of promise.

But there was something terribly wrong. Usually such a meal was filled with gay conversation, teasing and laughter, but that day there was none. Mother was too exhausted to talk much, Dad was still biting his lower lip thinking of the mince pie that was not to be, and I was thinking only of Pete Halfshoes and his can of pork and beans. When Dad passed me my plate heaped high with turkey, stuffing, and a lot of other things I felt I could not eat a single bite of it. But I did, of course. We Gages had to eat everything on the plate whether we liked it or not, and besides I was very hungry since I'd had my breakfast many hours before. Nevertheless, every single mouthful made me feel terribly guilty. It wasn't fair!

No one took a second helping except my father, and I think he did so only to postpone the challenge presented by the pumpkin rather than the mince pie. Having consumed his big drumstick (Dad always got the dark meat), he carved himself two big slices from the thigh, ladled the brown gravy onto a mound of stuffing, toyed with his Waldorf salad, ate two more oysters, and then, as my mother watched, forked up the tip of the pumpkin pie tentatively. "Not bad, Madam!" he said as he ate all the rest of it. "Not bad!" Patting his bulging vest, he left the table to take a siesta on the couch in the living room. Mother gave me a wink. All was well!

But it wasn't! While I helped Mother with the dishes I couldn't get Pete Halfshoes out of my head. Then came the terrible thought that I should steal the other drumstick and take it up to the old Indian. No, no, no! I couldn't do that! It would be stealing and we Gages didn't ever steal, nor lie, nor cheat, nor shoot does. I vividly recalled how only two years before, when I was only six, that I'd come back from Flynn's store with a pocketful of dried prunes I'd swiped from the open keg by the candy counter. When I innocently offered one of the prunes to my mother and she found out how I'd gotten them all hell broke loose. What a lecture! What shaming! "Gages never, never steal!" she told me. "I'll not tell your father. He'd spank you too hard but promise me you'll never do anything like that again." I promised. Then she unscrewed the bottom of my little cast iron bank, took out a quarter and sent me up to Mr. Flynn with it along with my apologies.

Despite that promise I just felt I had to steal that drumstick for the old Indian, my friend. So after my mother had gone to her bedroom to rest from her long labors and Dorothy was still sleeping in her crib and my brother Joe was building little houses out of dominoes, I sneaked into the pantry, twisted off the big drumstick, wrapped it in newspaper, hid it under my shirt, then went to Pete's cabin.

I found Pete there with his pet skunk on his knee, stroking her white striped pelt. When I pulled the package out from under my shirt and opened it I blurted, "This is for you, Pete. Happy Thanksgiving! I'd have brought you a piece of mince pie too but we didn't have any mincemeat this year because Dad didn't get his buck." I could tell that the old Indian was touched though, of course, his face didn't move a muscle. "You good boy, Cully," was all he said.

It sure seemed like a long way home overwhelmed as I was by the enormity of my good deed. I was a thief. How I dreaded the coming of suppertime! And when it did come I was rigid with shame and fright as my mother put the carcass of the turkey before my father. He gave it a hard look. "Where's my drumstick?" he roared. "Where's the other drumstick? If the dog's gotten into the pantry again I swear I'll shoot the bugger." It was time to take my bitter medicine.

"No, Dad," I said trembling. "It wasn't the dog. It was me. I stole your drumstick."

He couldn't believe his ears. "What?" he roared. "What did you say?"

Somehow through my tears I managed to tell him about Pete Halfshoes eating nothing but pork and beans from a can and how bad I felt and how unfair it was for Pete to have so little when we had so much and that was why I stole the drumstick.

Mother gave Dad a fierce look. "No Cully," she said, "That wasn't stealing. That was sharing and I'm very proud of you."

Dad stopped biting his lip. "Yeah," he said. "That's right. I'm glad you did it but don't you ever do it again without telling us. Besides there's plenty of dark meat left on the thigh."

Whew!

But the best part was yet to come. At exactly seven o'clock of the second morning after Thanksgiving my father left the kitchen to go out on the back steps to blow his nose mightily and greet the new day as was

24

his custom (It was said in the village that some of our people set their watches when they heard that mighty blast.) But hardly had he opened the door when he returned. "Edyth," he yelled excitedly. "Come see! Someone has left a whole hindquarter of deer in the entry. Now we can have venison mincemeat pie again." Mother didn't move from her chair. She just sighed, a long sigh that sounded like the suds going down our kitchen sink.

"I wonder who brought it," Dad mused. "Probably someone who hasn't been able to pay me what he owes. Lord knows there are plenty of them. Wonder who it was."

I knew!

SAVE THE LAST DANCE FOR ME

In the old days about the beginning of this century Tioga wasn't the sleepy little forest village it is today. It was mainly a mining town, almost a little city, with more than a thousand men working in double shifts. It boasted three stores, five churches and a ten-bed whorehouse. Located at the junction of a north-south and an east-west railroad, the roar and whistles of locomotives hauling passengers, freight and ore filled the air day and night. There were two post offices, one at the bottom of our hill street and the other on top near the Big Mine, so called because it was the biggest and deepest of the five working mines in the area. Why, at one time, it was the deepest iron mine in the world, over a mile deep and at its lower levels so warm the men worked naked to the waist.

William Trelawney was Captain of the Big Mine. In his prime at forty-five, he ran the operation with an iron hand. A rough, tough man, the men called him, but fair. He could sure put out the ore. Unlike some of the other mining captains, Cap'n Bill didn't just sit in his office and give orders; he seemed to be everywhere, on surface and underground too. Slow to hire and quick to fire, he dominated the workings. "Cap'n coming! Cap'n coming!" When that news came over the mysterious information grapevine down the shaft, the trammers hurried, the carpenters hammered fast on the cribbing, and the drillers swung their sledges harder. Cap'n Bill tolerated no shirkers. "A driver-man" the miners called him.

Even the shift bosses feared him. One of them, Erick Salmonen, still with a hangover from a weekend drunk, was discovered sitting on an empty powder keg in one of the raises on level-nine just ten minutes before the half-hour noon break. Cap'n Bill knocked him senseless, dragged him to the cage and signalled the hoist engineer to pull up. "You'll never work in my mine again," he roared. "You're fired!" But the word went around that Cap'n Bill made arrangements for one of the other mining captains to hire Erick. After all, Erick had eleven kids and was usually a good worker.

The men thought that was fair enough. Moreover, they knew that Cap'n Bill cared for them. When, as happened three or four times each year, a man was killed, he always made sure the widow got a good pension and permission to live in the company house as long as she wanted. When one of the miners got hurt and had to go to my father's hospital, Cap'n Bill always went to see him there on the cot. Also, the men appreciated it when Cap'n Bill persuaded the mine superintendent, Henry Thompson, to put electric arc lights all along our hill street so they wouldn't have to walk in the dark to and from work in the winter months, and to put a pool table and bowling alley in the clubhouse that they could use if they had the money. "Ay, he's a hard man," our people said, "but he's got a soft side."

Captain Bill didn't look hard, except for a jutting lower jaw. Powerfully built but short in stature, he looked like Santa Claus without the beard or belly. Laugh lines crinkled out from his eyes onto a very rosy face and off the job the eyes were always twinkling. He liked little kids and they liked him, perhaps because he always carried in his pocket a handful of jelly beans to give them, or perhaps because he and his wife had no children of their own.

But I must tell you something about Eleanore, his wife. Certainly the most beautiful woman in Tioga, she was also among the gayest. My mother loved her visits to our house because she always made everyone feel happy. Some people are just that way. More educated than her husband who adored her, she had a gift for the right phrase that always put one at ease immediately. Eleanore was also a caring person, doing one good deed after another. If someone became ill, Eleanore was soon there to bring a meal or offer comfort. The high school girls confided in her more than to their own mothers, scrutinized the fashionable clothing she wore, and tried to walk as gracefully as she did. No one, not even Aunt Lizzie, ever had said a bad thing about her. They couldn't!

The Trelawney's yard in summer was one of the show places in our village. From spring to fall it was a riot of flowers almost as colorful as the dresses Eleanore always wore. Back then, most of our women wore long black or brown dresses that they had to lift slightly whenever they encountered a cow pasty on the wooden sidewalks. Not Eleanore! Hers were yellow, red or blue and barely touched the top of her shapely ankles. Soon the French Canadian girls downtown were emulating her. Not the Finns, though. Following three steps behind their husbands on the way to church in their long dark skirts, they kept to the old ways while secretly wishing they had the nerve to wear clothes like Eleanore Trelawney's.

Even after the snow came, the Trelawney house was full of flowers because they had turned a south-facing bay window into a little conservatory full of ferns, coleus, African violets and the blooming bulbs that Eleanore had forced. A few of the houses in our town had a single pork and bean can with a red geranium on the window sill to counteract the black and white of winter but every window in the Trelawney house had three or four pots of them - even the windows upstairs.

I was in that house only once, but I remember those flowers and the lighted candles on the table and especially the little reed organ in the corner. Both Cap'n Bill and Eleanore loved to sing in harmony, he with a deep bass and she in a contralto. Sometimes in the summer months we kids would go to their fence to hear their duets at eventide. They also occasionally sang them at a church service too because both were good Methodists and participated in all the church activities. That helped to counteract Aunt Lizzie's torturing of the high notes when the choir sang.

The Trelawneys also loved to dance, mainly the waltz and two step, and they belonged to the dance club in Ishpeming that my folks did. With the Gages and the Thompsons and a mining engineer and his wife, once a month they'd take the train to Ishpeming, stay overnight at the Mather Inn, have dinner, and go to a cotillion sponsored by the Ishpeming couples in the club. I remember how beautiful my mother looked in a new blue and white dancing gown and how handsome my father was as they left for the railroad station, leaving us kids in the stern care of Fannie Hedetniemi. I knew that Dad would rather be hunting or fishing but he knew how important it was for mother to dress up and be glamorous again.

The four couples were very close friends and once a month they held parties in their homes where they played whist. When they came to our house mother spent a week in preparation for the event. We, of course, were banished to our rooms upstairs but we'd listen through the register to their gaiety until we couldn't keep our eyes open any longer. Yes, before the big cave-in happened and the mine closed, the winters weren't too bad in Tioga, Mother always said.

But even before the cave-in things changed. Two feet of snow came down in a single night late in October, and it never left until the next May. Shoveling out, Cap'n Bill Trelawney suddenly died. Cardiac arrest was what my father wrote on the death certificate after he'd been called and had failed to resuscitate him. "I should have suspected it," he told my shocked and weeping mother. "Bill's ruddy complexion should have alerted me to the possibility of high blood pressure, but he always seemed so healthy and hearty I just missed it. You'd better pull yourself together and go up to see Eleanore. She's in a bad way and has no family to comfort her. Stay as long as you need to. I'll call Stenrud, the undertaker, and make the necessary arrangements. I've also told Henry Thompson so he and his wife may be there."

Mother was gone all day, and when she returned at five to get our supper, I thought for the first time that she looked as though she were getting old. "Oh, John," she said to my father. "It was terrible. Eleanore can't cry and can hardly talk. Just sits there with a frozen face staring, staring. When I tried to hold her hand she pulled it away. I don't think she heard anything Eva Thompson and I said when we tried to console her. About the only time she talked at all was when she asked us to keep anyone from coming in and there were a lot of them bringing food. When the pastor insisted on entering about three o'clock despite her wishes, she just shut her eyes and probably her ears too. Just sat there stiffly and acted as though he weren't there. Oh John, if only she could cry!"

"She's in shock," my father said. "I've seen it before. Only time will help her overcome it, time and sleep. I'll go up there this evening and give her a strong sleeping pill or shot. She'd better not stay alone, though."

"No," replied mother. "Eva's with her now and I'll go up again right after supper and Mick's wife will be there from midnight on, but oh if we could only help her to weep."

The next morning at six o'clock I was awakened by two sounds, by that of the mine whistle blowing not the usual two times but eleven times, and by that of my Mother treading the pedal of her sewing machine in the sewing room next to my bedroom.

"Do you think it looks all right, John?" she asked my father holding up the black dress on which she'd been working. "After you left last night Eleanore did fall asleep in her chair so we put her to bed, then looked in her closet to see if she had anything black or dark to wear for the mourning and funeral. John, there wasn't a thing there except bright dresses and dancing gowns, not a single suitable thing she could wear. So I thought of this dark dress of mine and that I could take off the colored collar and sash. She's just my size, you know, and I'm sure it would fit if she would wear it. Oh, I hope she's got herself together for the hard time ahead."

At this time Tioga had no funeral home. Mr. Stenrud, the undertaker, kept his coffins and did his dirty work in the back room of

Callahan's store. Then the body was taken to the church in Mr. Marchand's horse-drawn hearse. I remember that hearse very clearly. It was a glassed-in box that could be fitted on a wagon in the summer and on a sleigh in winter. From the roof black tassels hung, almost like the fringe of our surrey and inside it were candelabra with candles lighting the coffin inside. Mr. Marchand and usually one of the mourners rode on a spring seat in front. In our Methodist church, the open coffin lay in state in the Epworth League room for the viewing and paying of last respects. A small room, the mourners often had a hard time squeezing between the coffin and the coal stove and the many urns of flowers sent up on the train from Ishpeming. The fire was kept going day and night in winter time because some family members of the deceased were expected to stay there to keep the corpse company and the candles lit. A cold long vigil!

But there were no family members. Cap'n Bill still had a brother and sisters and some nephews but they were in Cornwall, England, from which he had emigrated when in his late teens, while Eleanore, an only child, had lost her parents only a few years before. Since my folks and the Thompsons and the Hadleys, her closest friends, were taking turns staying with Eleanore, others had to be found to be with the casket. There were many volunteers. We took care of each other in the U.P. back then.

When Mother came back at noon to get our dinner, Dad, who'd been making house calls all morning, asked her how Eleanore was doing.

"Much better, John." she replied. "That long sleep you gave her really helped. She even drank some coffee and nibbled at a piece of toast, and watered her flowers. Also she could talk a little but not about Bill. When the Pastor came, she answered his questions. I hoped that when he gave a little prayer she might weep but she didn't. I think she's just denying the whole thing, pretending that nothing's happened. She appreciated the black dress I gave her but put a red rose on it, one of those you ordered to be sent up on the train from Ishpeming. And, John, she absolutely refuses to go with any of us to see Bill in the coffin at church. We told her we could arrange it so no one else would be there so she could be alone with him, but she was stubborn. "No," she said, "No, no, no!" and she made us promise that there would be no wake. I hope we can get her to go to the funeral tomorrow morning. She's much better, really. Now if only she could cry!"

The next morning Mother and Dad had a little argument about whether I should go to the funeral service. "No, he isn't too young," my father said. "It's time he had the experience. Who knows? Death could come to us too and he'd better be prepared." So Mother took me with her to the church though she left me in a rear pew so she could join Dad and the Thompsons and Hadleys when they came with Eleanore to sit down front.

The church was full of people but it was totally quiet except for the soft moaning of the organ that Annie played. The coffin, covered with flowers, had been placed before the altar. Everyone kept their coats and boots on because it was chilly in there despite the fact that the two potbellied stoves had been kept going all night. There was no singing of hymns, just silence. When the preacher read something from the Bible and asked all of us to pray for the dear departed and began to talk about Cap'n Bill, suddenly Eleanore broke away and fled from the church.

Everything stopped. People looked at each other. Mother and Mrs. Thompson ran up the aisle in pursuit, with Dad and the other two men after them but not until Henry Thompson, our mine superintendent, gave the order to continue the service and "to bury him." Huddled there in the back pew I didn't know what to do, so I just sat there. Finally, the preacher asked all of us to pray for Eleanore, Annie played some more on the organ, and the pallbearers came to take the coffin away. I went home to find Dad hunting for a pry bar. "She's locked her door," he said. Finding it, he left the house but not until he'd ordered me to go to the graveyard. "Better see the rest of it," Dad said.

I got to the cemetery just as the pallbearers were unloading the heavy mahogany coffin from the hearse. A large deep hole, perhaps eight by four feet, had been freshly dug in the ground with the dirt heaped up at both ends. The snow had been shoveled out around it and perhaps twenty men, mostly miners of the night shift, were standing in the little clearing talking quietly. I heard one of them say, "Well, it's a good thing the ground wasn't frozen yet. Poor Cap'n Bill would have to wait in the crypt till spring breakup." He nodded to an ugly wooden log cabin without windows and a padlocked door behind them. "Yep," said his listener. "Better to be in the ground."

The pallbearers grunted as they stooped, then kneeled to lower the coffin into the grave. Then the preacher came over, read something from a black book that I couldn't hear, and asked the men if anyone had anything to say about the deceased. They shuffled uneasily, holding their caps in their hands, until one of them said, "Cap'n Bill was a good boss. Hard but good." A murmur of agreement occurred. Then another man said, "Tough to die so young. In his prime, too." When no one else said anything, the preacher said a short prayer, and motioned the grave diggers to start shoveling. It seemed a shame to see that dirt going on top of the coffin. That was all. Everybody went home.

Mother wasn't home much the next few days except to prepare our meals and to put us kids in bed. She sure looked awfully tired. "John," she said to my father one morning, "I don't know how much longer things can go on like this. Your sleeping pills let Eleanore sleep but she's not eating anything, though there's enough food in the house for a month with all the dishes people have brought her. And she won't talk at all now. Just sits and stares again, hour after hour, wearing that black dress I gave her but without the flower. And she doesn't even water her own flowers now and we have to do it. Today I tried to help her weep at last by telling about all the good times she and Bill had with us, the picnics and dancing and such, but she just sat there. I'm all worn out, John."

"Yeah," said Dad, "It's been long enough. We can't let her spoil our lives too. She has to face up to it. Bill is in his grave and that's that! I've a mind to go up there and tell her so." Mother asked him to be gentle.

When Dad returned I could tell he was upset. "Well, I told her," he said. "Just laid it on the table. Said that though Bill was dead and buried she still had close friends who cared for her but that they couldn't be with her all the time, that she just had to start living again, that you and Eva and Mick's wife would come up for a short time each day to see if there was anything to do but that was all."

"How did she respond?" my mother asked.

"She didn't say a word. Just stared at me."

So it went on, day after day, for many weeks. Then one morning my father found Eleanore Trelawney dead on the couch in the living room, dressed in a beautiful red and white dancing gown and with scarlet dancing slippers on her feet.

As my father said when be filled out the death certificate to read 'cardiac arrest', "people do die of broken hearts." He did not mention the crumpled note he had found in Eleanore's clutched hand:

"Bill, save the last dance for me."

YARN FOR DEER CAMP

It was breakup time, the train from Milwaukee was many hours late, and a salesman who'd come up on the South Shore and Atlantic from Marquette was restless. Going up to the ticket window, he asked the station-master how much longer he'd have to wait. "God knows," replied that worthy. "Latest we've heard they've just pulled out of Pembine, Wisconsin. Got to go slow this time of year, you know, because of soft track. Why don't you go over to Higley's Saloon for two or three hours to pass the time? Just a block away west of here. False front building. You'll see the lights."

Lugging his two square bags, the salesman found his way and when he entered and bellied up to the bar he felt better. Lots of noise and laughter and people telling tales. All the regulars were there: Pete Half-Shoes in the corner of his booth, Pete Ramos already half snockered, Laf Bodine and Dinny Callahan playing cards at one of the tables, and ten or twelve other men nursing their beers. "What'll you have, stranger?" asked Higley, twirling the ends of his black mustache, "beer or whiskey?" The salesman looked over the array of fancy bottles behind Higley. "How about a shot of that Old Age Bourbon?" he suggested. "Naw," said Higley, "Them bottles got nothing in them but water. Just for show. You want whiskey, I got whiskey. Good rotgut right from the barrel." The salesman settled for a beer.

Two of the men beside him were talking about mosquitoes and mosquito dope. "They're going to be bad this year," one of them said. "Too much rain." "Can't be any worse than last year," said another. "Got so bad in June the cows quit giving milk because they had to keep their eyes shut and couldn't find grass to eat."

"Yeah," said a third man. "Never seen such big skeeters as last year. Over by Splatterdock Lake I had one chawing me that was an inch tall on my wrist. Left a hole as big as a deer fly."

"Oh hell, that's nothing," said a fourth, "Why up there by the Hayshed dam I..."

The stranger interrupted. "Yeah, that's nothing. Down in Wisconsin where I come from we got mosquitoes two, three inches tall in their stocking feet. We use them for muskie bait."

Our men grinned appreciatively. The lying had begun again; it would be a good evening. "What kind of dope do you use for them big Wisconsin mosquitoes?" a man asked, "Citronella or oil of pennyroyal?"

"Neither," said the salesman taking a big swallow from his mug. "Hell, those big Wisconsin mosquitoes drink citronella like soup. In June month to get any sleep at all we have to pull the covers over our heads and almost suffocate. Once I put a dish of citronella by my bed and right away a swarm of 'em come and drank the whole thing in five minutes."

"Sure must be bad, them Wisconsin skeeters," the man beside him said. "What do you do when you're out in the bush?"

"Well," said the salesman, "some wear helmets of fine screening over their heads and tucked in their shirts, and gauntlets of the same over their hands and wrists but the damned sketters get stuck in 'em and then you can't see too good. Kerosene is the only thing that really works."

"Kerosene?" asked his listener. "That'd burn your hide off you put it on yer skin. Worse than the mosquitoes."

"Naw, we don't put it on our skin," the salesman answered. "We put it on their tails and set fire to 'em." What a roar of laughter went up from the bar. This guy was good. "Yessiree," he concluded, "we've got the biggest damned skeeters in the whole country there in Wisconsin. Yeah, and the biggest liars too." The salesman grinned.

The men at the bar hadn't noticed that Slimber Vester, Tioga's best liar, had entered the saloon and heard the last of the salesman's tale but when they saw him they let out a yell. "Hey Slimber, this bird sez that they got the biggest liars in the world in Wisconsin. Tell him about the time you crossed the blue heron with a duck."

"Yeah," said another, "Tell 'im about that horse you taught to point

34

partridge or how you showed that there bullfrog to jump. Mister, see that big trout Mustamaya on the wall? Well, Slimber here caught that monster with a post-hole digger, he did, or so he sez. And how about Old Lunker that the bear swiped off you?"

"Now, boys, you know old Slimber allus tells the truth, the whole truth and nothing but the truth swelpme God." The old bugger's face assumed a modest expression. "Now I like listening to a good lie like them my friend here has been a-telling and bedamn he told 'em well. Yessiree! I just wish I had the gift he has but my mama, bless her, she's been dead fifty year now, made me swear I'd tell only the truth. Oh, mebbe I've stretched it a bit sometimes but I've kept my promise, swelpme. Trouble is these here bar bums don't know the truth when they hear it." A saintly look spread over old Slimber's rosy cheeks and what with his white hair and beard and all, he looked virtuous as hell.

The men waited and waited. What was wrong with the old coot? Didn't he see the challenge? Why the honor of Tioga and the whole U.P. was at stake. OK, buy him another beer.

Under the lubrication old Slimber finally spoke. "Mister," he said to the salesman, "I come in late and my hearing's not so good but how big were them there Wisconsin skeeters of yours?"

The stranger grinned. "Oh, two or three inches high," he said. "Maybe you got bigger ones around here?"

"Nope," answered Slimber. "We got lots of them especially over by my cabin at Mud Lake but I never seen one taller than an inch at most. But when I was in Alaska..." He stopped to fill his corncob pipe and light it as the onlookers nudged each other and grinned. "Here it comes," one whispered, "God help Wisconsin!" They knew Slimber had never been further from Tioga than Marquette.

Slimber continued. "Well, as I was a'saying, when I was up in Alaska I seen some considerable bigger. Everything in Alaska is bigger, bigger fish, bigger bear, even bigger cabbage."

"That's the truth," a man said. "I've been there and they got cabbages big around as a barrel, weigh maybe thirty pound."

"How did you happen to be in Alaska?" the salesman asked.

Slimber tamped his pipe with a tobacco-stained forefinger. "Spent two year up there a-hunting for gold," he answered. "Rough country that. Took me a year before I finds paydirt. No, not dirt, rock it was. Found me a good quartz seam next to greenstone that was full of little gold threads so I stake a claim, build me a cabin and make a sluice box on a creek entering a good-sized lake. Ever see a sluice box, Mister?"

"No, can't say I ever have," replied the salesman, "we've got big mosquitoes in Wisconsin but no gold. I hear there used to be some gold mines in the U.P. That so?"

"Yep," said Slimber. He went into a long dissertation on how in Alaska you got to blast out the rock, then sledge or grind it down fine, then put it in the sluice box where the running water washes out the impurities and lets the gold dust and nuggets collect in the grooves.

"But how about those Alaskan mosquitoes?" The salesman sounded a bit impatient.

"I'm a-comin' to that, Mister. Don't hurry an honest old man," he said, taking another big swallow of beer. "As I was saying, I'd just finished that sluice box and was beginning to put the crushed rock in it one afternoon when I hear a big zoom comin' out the west and another even bigger one comin' from the north and then they joined, they did, and made a noise like the ore train coming around the Wabik curve and down the hill. Awful quiet up there back in the bush and that there sound almost filled me my pants. Then I seen them circling, bigger than eagles, above me and when they landed about thirty feet away I made me a dive for the cabin."

The salesman's mouth fell open. "Not mosquitoes?" he asked, trembling a bit.

"The hell they weren't," said Slimber. "They was two of 'em, mebbe six or seven feet tall and with eyes big as dinner plates and red beaks three feet long. And they was looking at me hungry-like even when they was a comin' down. As I say, I made a dive for the cabin to slam the door but one of 'em stuck a big foot in so I couldn't close it." Slimber, always a master of suspense, refilled his corncob pipe and blew a smoke ring. He knew he had his listeners hooked.

"What happened then, you old bastard?" one of the men yelled angrily.

"What I do then? I rolled myself under the table hopin' they couldn't bend their knees to get at me. Didn't know then that them Alaskan mosquitoes have knees. Well, both of them come in the cabin and looked me over and they was so tall they had to come in through the door on their knees, they did. Gadamighty I was scared. Then I heard them a-talkin' to each other, arguing-like. 'Let's eat him here!' the bigger one said but the other one was all for lugging me outside. 'No!' said the big one, 'If we haul him outside, the blackflies will get 'im.' Well I seen I had to do something fast, so while they were jawing at each other I rolled over to the cellar trap door, dropped in and pulled it shut over me. Phew! Close call, that!"

The salesman was swallowing hard. "Gimme a double shot of that rotgut," he ordered and Higley obliged, downing a shot for himself.

"Well, there I was," Slimber continued. "I could see some 'cause of light that come from under the bottom log and I had the spare axe I always keep in the cellar in case my good one gets stole or lost. Thought come to me that mebbe I could use it to widen the hole, crawl out and then slam the door on the critters but no, the axe just bounced off, the ground being so froze."

"That's right!" said the man who'd been in Alaska. "Two feet down the dirt never thaws. Damned if he ain't telling the truth! They calls it permfrost."

Slimber didn't bat an eye. "Well boys, I was a-hoping they might leave. That trap door set pretty flush and I was a hanging onto it hard when they tried prying. You ought to heerd them a buzzing and cussing on the floor above me. 'I told you we shoulda hauled him outside,' one said. 'Aw, all we gotta do is drill down and then lift off the cover,' the other growled, and then I hear a terrible whine noise like when the big mine generator starts up, and then a red beak tip starts comin' through the wood. And then another..." Slimber relit his corncob.

"C'mon! C'mon, you old fart," Laf roared. "What happened?"

"Man's got to keep his head when he's in such a per, perdika, in such a fix," said Slimber. "And I did, that I did. I took the flat of the axe and bent them red beaks of theirs over into the wood and clinched them tight. Ever hear a mosquito holler, Mister? Them big devils yelped so loud they almost lifted the roof and they yanked and pulled. Up goes the door over my head. Sure felt naked, I did but I was safe. They couldn't get their beaks out of the wood and squawking something terrible they backed out of the cabin door dragging it after them. Pulled that there trap door right off the hinges, they did. So I got my shotgun and let them have it. Pow! Pow! Blew their damned heads off."

A big sigh swept down the bar. The men hated to have the lie end. But there was more to come.

"Sure was a-shaking once it was over," Slimber said. "Had to sit a spell on the chopping block before I started cleaning them. Did the smaller one first, the cock. Just like dressing out a deer. Had me a mind to get some roasts outa the breasts 'cause they had no drumsticks to speak of — just skinny legs full of scales. Well, that done, I started on the hen, the bigger one, seven feet long she was, and fat..."

Slimber tapped the ashes from his pipe and the men groaned. "Yeah, when I slit her belly, damned if nine blue-black eggs popped out and started rolling down the slope to the lake. Tried to stomp them cause I could see they wuz about ready to hatch, the shells being cracked and little beaks coming out, but I only got six of them, the other three getting into the lake before I could catch 'em. Sure hated seeing that, Mister. You know how skeeters breed in water."

There was a long silence finally interrupted by one of the men at the bar. "How about the gold, Slimber? How about the gold?"

"I dunno," he replied. "I got my gear and hightailed it out of there fast. Wasn't going to hang around till them three hatched!"

The salesman put a ten dollar bill on the bar. "Drinks for everyone," he told Higley and then turned to Slimber as he picked up his bags. "Sir," he said respectfully. "I'm a-going back to Wisconsin where the skeeters are puny and the liars are too."

The honor of Tioga and the U.P. had been upheld.

THE RECLAMATION
OF SCOTTY MC GEE

It had been a long rainy Sunday late in June and I'd been trying to read Dickens' *Martin Chuzzlewit* all afternoon. Lord, it was slow and tedious going. I would have quit but it was the only book in our house I hadn't read and besides with the mosquitoes and rain there was nothing to do outside. It wasn't bedtime yet. Dad had eaten his Sunday supper of a bowl of bread and milk, read all the *Chicago Tribune*, and smoked his fat cigar, so perhaps he might be in his storytelling mood. I sure hoped so. Much better than *Martin Chuzzlewit*, his tales about his patients were dandies. It was understood, of course, that no one in the family would ever dare tell them to another living soul. Even now I feel a little uneasy recounting them, but here are two that I remember.

"Old man Chivaud couldn't hold his liquor very well and one winter's night came staggering out of Higley's saloon, missed the road, and came down instead on the railroad tracks that parallel it. And got hit by the cowcatcher of the train coming down from the Copper Country! Good thing it was slowing down for the station, but even so it threw him twenty feet into a snowbank by the freight depot. People saw it happen and when they ran over to see if he were dead they found Chivaud all crumpled up and moaning, so they got the stretcher from the baggage room and lugged him up the hill to the hospital and laid him on the table in the emergency room.

When I got there Chivaud was still alive and breathing though his eyes were closed. Pulse was all right, so we began to undress him to see the injuries. You know how these French Canadians dress for winter with one layer of clothes over the other. Well, we peeled off his bearskin overcoat, then two sweaters, a flannel shirt, two pairs of pants and his long filthy underwear. There wasn't a bruise on the old bugger, nothing wrong at all. When I told him so, old Chivaud rose up and grinned. "Oui, I know," he said, "but, Doctaire, me, I have a fine ride."

The other tale was Dad's maggot story. Sometimes, to tease my Mother he'd begin to tell it when we had a dinner guest, perhaps one of the lady school teachers, "John," she would say, "Don't tell that awful story or I'll leave the table." Here it is.

"On a hot summer day they brought in a lumberjack who'd cut a big gash in his leg with an axe. His dirty long underwear was so crusted with blood I just cut off the lower part of it and found one of the nastiest wounds I've ever seen. They'd wrapped the leg with a dirty dishtowel too and smeared the cut with axle grease and Lord knows what else. How many times have I told them not to put anything on such a wound but they just don't listen. Must have been many hours since he cut it because a lot of infection had already set in. What a mess! Bloody pus and dirt and inflammation had appeared, — even streaks of red radiating from the cut. We put the jack on the operating table and I had the men hold him still while I poured in peroxide and tried to scrape and swab the junk out. Took a long time and he was screaming before I was through. Couldn't blame him! Finally I put on a wet dressing, bandaged it, and told him to come back the next day to have it dressed again.

"Well, the lumberjack didn't show up then or the day after that either, so I sent some men to look for him. Knowing that I hadn't been able to get all the stuff out of the cut I was worried that the infection would be roaring again. Well, they found the coot back of our slaughter house, still half drunk, and I was thinking amputation when they brought him in. But you know what? Although he'd torn off the bandages and dressing, the leg looked pretty good overall. I found out why when I squeezed it and out came one maggot right after another. Must have been eight or nine of them and that wound was clean as a whistle. No pus, no proud flesh, no inflammation at all. Those maggots had eaten all the crap and cleaned it perfectly after the blowflies' eggs had hatched when he lay there in the hot sun. Thought I might write it up for a medical journal but never did. Later I read once that others had discovered the same thing, that during World War I they'd even raised sterile maggots to put in gunshot wounds."

It was stories like those that I was hoping to hear as I made myself inconspicuous as possible on the couch behind him pretending to be reading *Martin Chuzzlewit*. Yawning, he asked my Mother casually how the morning sermon had gone.

"It was awful, John," she replied. "We had another traveling evangelist who accused us of all the sins in the book, begged us to repent right then and there, and painted the whole church with fire and brimstone."

"Oh, oh," Dad exclaimed. "That means I'll be seeing old Scotty McGee tomorrow at office hours."

"Why do you say that?" my Mother asked.

"McGee has a classic case of cardiac neurosis," Dad explained. "He's certain that he's going to die at any time of heart trouble, and convinced that when he does he'll go to hell."

"Oh no," my Mother protested. "He's such a nice old man. No one goes to church more regularly. I did think he seemed very thin and sickly yesterday. Of course he must be in his late seventies..."

"He's seventy-eight," Dad interjected, "and in remarkably good shape for a man his age. I've examined him thoroughly several times in the last several years when he's come up complaining of heart trouble - usually after one of your preachers has scared him - but the pulse has always been strong and I couldn't find the slightest thing wrong when I listened to his heart. One time, thinking I might be missing something, I gave him some nitroglycerin to take if he had any pain and he said it just made him worse. It always does make the heart thump slower and stronger for a few moments but it always relieves any anginal pain. Moreover, Scotty says the pain was sharp like a toothache and when I asked where it was located he pointed to his left breast, not at the midline where it should be. McGee tells me it's worse at night rather than after hard effort which doesn't make sense either. Hypochondria, that's what it is. All in his head."

"But he's so thin, John, and now he walks with a stoop rather than erectly as he always did."

"He should," Dad said impatiently. "Lives on hardtack, bologna, coffee and a bit of whiskey now and then. I hear too that this year he's not planted a garden nor begun to put up any wood for next winter. Like all of us he used to do a lot of fishing and hunting, but for some time now he hasn't. Just stays in his cabin reading the bible and talking to himself. Hypochondriacal depression, that's what he's got and he'll probably manage to make his fears of dying come true if he doesn't watch out. But I say again, he's healthy as a horse physically. Probably in better shape than I am."

Dad's prediction was incorrect. Mr. McGee didn't show up at office-hour time. Instead he was sitting on his front stoop talking to himself. "No point bothering Doctor, McGee. He can't help you. Pretty soon you're a-going to die and you know it. You've had your time, yeah seventy-eight years of it, and that's long enough for an old crock like you. Got no wife; got no kids to mourn you either. You don't owe nobody nothing......"

He was interrupted by a yelping and yapping coming down the street as a dog with a bunch of cans tied to its tail tore down and the cans got stuck in a hole in McGee's picket fence. McGee hurried over to it. "Why it's just a pup!" he exclaimed. "Poor little fella. Damn kids to do a stunt like that. Ought to be a law agin it." Taking out his jackknife and talking soothingly he cut off the cans and the dog turned over on its back in supplication and fatigue. "That's all right; that's all right now, dog," he said, picking it up in his old arms and carrying it to the stoop where finally it stopped whimpering and began to lick his hand.

McGee looked it over. Not much of a dog, really and not much more than half grown. "Mixed stuff!" commented the old man, using the U.P. term for unknown ancestry. "Got the bow legs of a hound, the fur and tail of a spaniel, but damn if the head ain't that of a terrier. A Scotch terrier if I ever seen one." Why it looked like the head of Tam O'Shanter, the dog he'd had as a boy in Scotland a million years ago. For a moment he was tempted just to keep it. Might be company to have a dog around the house. Something to talk to. But no, it belonged to somebody else up the street and a sick old man had no right to have a dog depend on him. Why he might be dead come morning! So Scotty McGee led the mutt outside the fence, shut the gate, then went into the house to read his bible.

An hour later the dog was still there whimpering and because it had begun to sprinkle McGee brought it into the house, getting a face licking in the process. "Pore little critter's still scared," McGee said. "Guess I'll have to keep him overnight and take him uptown tomorrow to find where he lives."

It rained for three days and when it ended Old Man McGee was just about hooked. No Name, that was what he called the dog, had utterly delighted him, chasing its silly little tail in circles, offering to shake hands with uplifted paw, putting his head against the old man's leg and looking soulfully up into his eyes. Although McGee had made a bed for him out of an old Mackinaw, before morning the pup was beside him on the blankets. For a change he'd slept all night and hadn't had his usual three daily naps because it was just too interesting watching the little devil. How he liked to be stroked from the tail upward and rubbed around the ears. How he liked to be tickled on the belly just in front of a hind leg so the whole leg would start vibrating! How his silly tail waggled when McGee tossed an old sock and he brought it back for praising!

No Name was housebroken too, whining at the door to be let out, and whining again to be let in so the old man could wrap a towel around him and make him dry again. Feeding was a problem though. When McGee gave him a piece of the hardtack he'd broken off the black wheel the dog nosed it, dropped it on the floor, picked it up then dropped it again at his feet. "Guess yer teeth aren't hard enough yet," McGee said

41

to the dog. "Mine aren't so good either being old as I am. Mebbe you want it soaked in coffee too?" But the pup wouldn't try to eat it — just looked up at the old man with sad eyes. "Gotta get ye a bone, No Name; Gotta get ye a bone!" he said but all he had in the house was bologna and some korpua so the dog got those and wolfed them down. That made it so thirsty it drank from the water pail. "Smart dog!" McGee said admiringly. He said it again that evening when he read aloud as usual from the dog-eared bible and the pup cocked its head first to the right and then to the left, listening. "Damned if he don't know what I'm a-reading," McGee exclaimed.

When the rain stopped and the sun shone brightly, the old man sure hated the thought of trying to find No Name's owner. He hadn't been so happy in a long time. Why, he'd even laughed aloud at the pup's antics several times. Maybe he ought to keep him. "Nope, McGee," he said aloud. "Nope. 'Twouldn't be honest and besides 'twouldn't be fair if I keeps him and then go off an die on the little bugger." He realized with a start that he hadn't been thinking much about dying for some time and had been feeling really good. Moreover, his arthritic hand hadn't even hurt a bit doing all that scratching of No Name's hide.

Should he take the dog along with him? McGee didn't want to. Dreaded the long walk back alone if he did find where the pup belonged. But they had to see to recognize him, so in the afternoon, with No Name following at his heels, the old man went up our long hill street peering in every yard to see if there were any dogs resembling the puppy and stopping people to ask if anyone had lost a dog. No, they told him. Probably just another stray. Tioga had more dogs than people in those days, more dogs than they really could afford to feed.

McGee made one more try. At the post office he went in and asked Annie if she knew anyone who'd lost a dog. Annie knew everything that went on in town but no, she hadn't.

Going home, McGee stopped at my father's hospital knowing it was office-hour time. No one was in the anteroom waiting, so he went in. "Doctor," he said, "I gotta ask you something. How long you think I got before I croak? How much time kin you give me? Six months, one year or what days?" He explained about the dog and his concern for it in the event of his death. Dad examined him carefully, listened to his heart, and gave him some purple pills.

That night after supper I heard Dad telling Mother about it. "As I just said, Scotty wasn't worrying about himself so much as he was about the dog. Just wanted to be sure he'd live long enough to take care of it. I knew that dog right away. Belongs to the Pelkies. Saw it last week when I was up there looking at Mrs. Pelkie's hernia. They've got some mean kids and when I came out of the house they had that puppy cornered between the barn and the woodshed and were throwing big stones at it. I gave them hell and stopped it."

"I hope you didn't tell Mr. McGee who owned it, John."

"Of course not," Dad replied. "The old man's bound to give it a better home than its got now."

"How long did you tell him he had yet to live?" asked Mother.

Dad grinned. "I thought I'd use a little psychology on him to try to get the thought of dying out of his head. So first of all I gave him a thorough examination using the stethoscope to listen to his heart, thumping his back good, and checking his reflexes. Then I took down one of my big medical books and pretended to read it. 'Yes,' I said, 'that's it!' Then I told McGee he had a rare disease called cardiac hypochondria which was always fatal. 'I knew it,' said McGee, 'but how long, Doctor, how long have I left?' I looked in the medical book again. 'Mr. McGee, it says here that there's a powerful new medicine that can hold off death for three or perhaps even more years providing the patient cooperates by taking it every day. Fortunately, I have some of that medication, Mr. McGee,' and I gave him a bottle of those big purple pills I rolled and dried on the cookie sheet on your kitchen range last week."

"Oh John, you didn't! Those huge horrible looking pills? You told me they were just aspirin."

"Yep," said Dad grinning. "Just aspirin - salycilic paste colored a bilious purple with potassium permanganate and tincture of gentian and big as a marble. Horse pills! The placebo of placebos! The few people I've tried them on swear by them. Doesn't hurt them and the aspirin may relieve a bit of pain, but it's the placebo effect that counts especially on hypochondriacs like McGee."

"To make sure," Dad continued, "I told McGee that these were very powerful pills. Under no circumstances was he to take more than one each morning. "With milk," I added. He'd told me he'd been living on hardtack, korpua and bologna with an occasional can of beans. Sure looked it too. With his shirt off, his ribs showed. For that matter, the dog was starved too."

"Oh what a shame!" exclaimed Mother. "Is he that poor, John?"

"I don't know, Edyth. I understand he has a small pension from the mining company but he's a Scot and I'd bet he has a little cash stacked away somewhere. Enough for milk anyway. He sure winced when I told him the pills were terribly expensive, a dollar a pill."

"Oh John! You didn't say that!" My Mother was shocked.

"Yes I did. Had to impress upon him the value of those pills, but I also told him I'd give them free if he'd come up and sweep out the dispensary and office and waiting room each week. That will get him out of the house and give him some exercise. I did something else too. Having heard that he hadn't planted a garden, I told him to go help Widow Johnson with hers. Went by there the other day and saw that she'd overplanted her potatoes and beans but hadn't tended them. Just a mess of pursley and quackgrass. I told McGee to offer to weed and take care of them in exchange for half the crop. Plenty there for both of them."

McGee walked down the hill street feeling better than he had for a

43

long time. "Three, four years, mebbe more," he said aloud half to himself and half to No Name. "That's a-plenty. You're a-going to stay with McGee and he'll take care of you good, he will. "But McGee, you got to get milk right away so you kin take them big pills."

When he reached his house, the old man went directly to the cellar and the two lard cans that were hidden behind the boards. The bigger one was the savings one, the other the spending can. McGee had never taken a single bill out of the savings can. Never! Even before he'd retired from the mine he'd religiously put money in it from every pay check he received and only opened it thereafter to toss in at least one dollar bill from each month's pension. There had been many times when he'd been tempted, such as when the coffee ran out, but he'd never given in. No sir! "Lord, McGee, you've got a lot of money here," he said. "Damn near rich, ye are. What you saving for anyway? Got no heirs. Lots more than you need for burying money. Take a chunk of it, McGee, and buy milk and bones for yer dog!"

So he did. With No Name trotting by his side, the old man went to Flynn's store and bought some bread, two quart bottles of milk, two pounds of ground beef, a slab of bacon, a big bone and a pail of coffee. Feeling hungry for the first time in months, he fried up half of the ground beef, gave half to the dog and ate it with store bread and butter. And with milk. "Ye haven't tasted milk in a long time, McGee," he said. "Better than java or even whiskey, it is." The puppy had wolfed down his meat in a hurry and was begging for more. "No, dog, that's enough," McGee said, "but mebbe ye'd like some milk too?" No Name wagged his tail and when the old man set a saucerful out for him he lapped it up quickly. "Pore little critter, he's starved," McGee said and gave him the rest of the bologna. "We'll both be eating better from now on," he said.

Well that was the beginning of some wonderful years for McGee and Tam O'Shanter. Yes, that was the dog's name now. Once the old man was certain that the purple pills were doing him some real good and when he was sure no one would be claiming the pup, McGee one evening performed the naming ceremony. Sitting in the rocking chair by the box stove and spreading his legs he called the dog to him. "Time you had a proper Christian name, pup," he said. "Old McGee's been thinking on it 'cause yer his dog and he's yer man. Got to be a Scot name too 'cause we both got Scot blood in us. Had a dog in the old country when I was a boy look like you and his name was Tam, Tam O'Shanter. Name come from one of Robbie Burns' poems we used to recite in school. How did it go, McGee?" The old man screwed up one eye and thought hard. All I kin remember is bits. Lessee now..."

Tam looked up soulfully as McGee scratched both their heads. "Och! Ye know the poem, McGee. The one about how Tam O'Shanter rode his horse Maggie to the tavern against the wishes of his wife. Kate her name was. Ah yes.

'She told thee well thou was a blellum,
a blethering, blustering, drunken blellum,
that from November till October
on market day thou was not sober!'

"Ay, that's how it went.

'Gathering her brows like gathering storm
Nursing her wrath to keep it warm..'

"Oh, I forgit what else except that Tam met a mess of devils and witches who chased him home and pulled Maggie's tail off at the bridge. Doesn't matter, I reckon, but from now on yer name is Tam. Understand?" Tam thumped his tail on the floor and raised a paw. They shook hands. No more No Name.

The two became inseparable and provided a common sight on our hill street as McGee with the dog at his heels made their daily journey to my Dad's hospital or the store. Oh there were times when McGee had to shut Tam in the house to go to church or such. Once he'd tried to smuggle Tam there under his overcoat, but Charley Olafson saw the bulge and shooed them out. In summer months they often could be seen on Lake Tioga too after Alphone DeCaire, who'd caught a basket of brook trout and his wife refused to cook them because they'd been having too many, brought them to McGee. Tam liked fish and the old man tried to take him with him after trout but that didn't work out because of the splashings. In a boat, though, Tam was fine, sitting silently in the stern like a Captain of the Fleet, while McGee rowed and trolled for pike. Didn't move a muscle until a big fish was thrashing in the bottom but then he barked like hell in celebration.

Hating to spend the money for milk, McGee thought of getting a cow but then he heard that Mr. Salmi was in such bad shape he couldn't make hay so McGee did it for him and for milk and butter. Good exercise that! Tam liked eggs too and the old man thought of getting some chickens. He had the coop for them and some years before had all the eggs he needed, but Mrs. Johnson whose garden he now kept in fine shape often gave him a half dozen eggs when the hens were laying, also potatoes and rutabagas when the frosts came.

Tam had to stay in the house too when McGee got out his old rifle to hunt deer, though he got rewarded by having lots of bones to chew and venison to eat as well as a lot of extra petting. McGee was happier than he'd ever been. He had company to talk to, to bed with, to share his meals with. Religiously he swallowed one of those monster purple pills each day and had no fear of dying.

One afternoon next spring Dad called Mother's attention to the old man as he and Tam were walking up the street to the store. "Look at the old coot, Edyth," he commanded. "Look at him gallop! Why, he's walking as fast as any young kid. And see how he's filled out, the dog too. Lots of exercise and better food and my purple pills have made him a new man. That psychology is good stuff."

45

Seven years later when I had to leave Tioga to go to college the two of them were still in fine shape, still going strong, and still inseparable.

Was it the dog or the purple pills?

THE U.P. DIALECT

Phonetic Symbol	Key Words English	Phonetics	Phonetic Symbol	Key Words English	Phonetics

Consonants

Phonetic Symbol	English	Phonetics	Phonetic Symbol	English	Phonetics
b	beg, tub	bɛg tʌb	p	paper, damper	pepɚ dæmpɚ
d	do, and	du ænd	r	run, far	rʌn fɑr
f	fan, scarf	fæn skɑrf	s	send, us	sɛnd ʌs
g	grow, bag	gro bæg	t	toe, ant	to ænt
dʒ	judge, enjoy	dʒʌdʒ ɪndʒɔɪ	ʃ	shed, ash	ʃɛd æʃ
h	hem, inhale	hɛm ɪnhel	tʃ	cheap, each	tʃip itʃ
k	kick, uncle	kɪk ʌŋkl̩	θ	thin, tooth	θɪn tuθ
l	let, pal	lɛt pæl	ð	then, breathe	ðɛn brið
l̩	apple, turtle	æpl̩ tɝtl̩	v	vow, have	vau hæv
m	men, arm	mɛn ɑrm	w	wet, twin	wɛt twɪn
m̩	autumn, wisdom	ɔtm̩ wɪzdm̩	hw	when, white	hwɛn hwaɪt
n	nose, gain	noz gen	j	you, yet	ju jɛt
n̩	sudden, curtain	sʌdn̩ kɝtn̩	ʒ	pleasure, vision	plɛʒɚ vɪʒən
ŋ	wrong, anger	rɔŋ æŋgɚ	z	zoo, ooze	zu uz

Vowels

Phonetic Symbol	English	Phonetics	Phonetic Symbol	English	Phonetics
a*	ask, rather	ask raðɚ	ɒ*	log, toss	lɒg tɒs
ɑ	father, odd	fɑðɚ ɑd	ɝ	earn, fur	ɝn fɝ
e	make, eight	mek et	ɜ*	earn, fur	ɜn fɜ
æ	sat, act	sæt ækt	ɚ	never, percale	nɛvɚ pɚkel
i	fatigue, east	fətig ist	u	truth, blue	truθ blu
ɛ	red, end	rɛd ɛnd	ʊ	put, nook	pʊt nʊk
ɪ	it, since	ɪt sɪns	ʌ	under, love	ʌndɚ lʌv
o	hope, old	hop old	ə	about, second	əbaut sɛkənd
ɔ	sauce, off	sɔs ɔf			

Diphthongs

[aɪ]	sigh, aisle	[saɪ aɪl]	[ɔɪ]	coy, oil	[kɔɪ ɔɪl]
[au]	now, owl	[nau aul]			

*These sounds are only rarely used in General American speech, but are common in the East and South. General American speech uses [æ] for [a], [ɔ] for [ɒ], and [ʃ] for [ʒ].

Reprinted with permission from An Introduction to General American Phonetics by Charles Van Riper. Harper and Row, New York.

Dad had just finished his breakfast when the box phone (the kind you had to crank to call Genevieve at Central), rang. He groaned. Dad always groaned when he heard the phone ring. "Wonder what wart thinks he's sick now?" he said, picking up the receiver. "Yes, yes. Where did you say your farm was? All right. I'll be there when I get there - sometime this morning, I hope." Turning to Mother, he said, "emergency call from a man who has a homestead near Black River; thinks his wife's dying. Two hours each way, I suppose, so don't expect me for dinner. I'd appreciate having a sandwich." Then to me he said, "Cully, you hitch up the horse to the buckboard and put some hay and oats in back. And then you get the mail. It won't be here until after nine but I want it when I get home."

Not much mail. Oh the *Chicago Tribune*, of course, and M.C. Flynn's monthly bill for groceries, and a long envelope from the University of Michigan.

When he returned early that afternoon, Dad had some milk and a piece of pie, then opened the long envelope first. He silently read the letter for a long time, then read it aloud to Mother. "Dear Dr. Gage: May I introduce myself? I am James R. Johnson, Ph.D., professor of linguistics at your alma mater, the University of Michigan. Planning on retirement next year, I am desirous of doing one last research, a definitive study of the U.P. dialect. To my knowledge, no other scholar has investigated this subject although many have mentioned that it exists because of the melting-pot effect produced by nationals of many lands who with their children emigrated to your land to work in the mines and forests. Seeking a site that might fit the purposes of my investigation, I found that Tioga, located in the center of the Upper Peninsula, with its iron mines and extensive lumbering operations, might well be the place where I could begin my linguistic analysis. I secured your name from our alumni association as a possible initial contact and I wonder, sir, if you could provide me with the name of a hotel or rooming house in your village so I can make the necessary arrangements. I plan to stay at least a week and am prepared to spend much longer if the opportunities to do this research are promising. I include a reprint of a similar study I did on the Creole dialect of Southern Louisiana. Help me if you can. Sincerely yours, James R. Johnson, Ph. D., Professor of Linguistics, the University of Michigan."

"You're going to answer him, aren't you John?" Mother asked.

"Of course I will," Dad replied. "If it weren't for the U. of M. I'd never become a doctor. I owe them a lot but I don't know what to say. There's no hotel in Tioga since the mine closed and the Beacon House shut down. No rooming house either."

"Aunt Lizzie sometimes takes boarders," Mother replied, her blue eyes twinkling. She knew how he'd respond.

"No, no, no, no!" Dad roared. "I wouldn't wish that on my worst enemy. Aunt Lizzie would clack him to death, the old hag." My father, to put it mildly, did not like Aunt Lizzie, our town gossip and troublemaker. Couldn't stand the old buzzard!

"Well, why don't you invite him to stay with us for a short time. I think he said he planned initially to spend a week exploring the possibilities of his research, and perhaps by then we could find someone to take him in or he could go to an Ishpeming hotel and do his research around there. He could have Grandma Van's room and one more mouth to feed for a week wouldn't be any problem. But what's linguistics, John?"

"Don't really know," Dad answered. "The study of languages and their grammar and pronunciation maybe. I may know more about it when I read that reprint of his, but that's a good idea. I'll tell him he can stay with us for a short time."

Mother was delighted. "Oh, it will be good, John, to have some civilized conversation again. Not that these aren't fine people in Tioga. They are! But do you realize that you, Mr. Donegal, and Father Hassel are the only men in town with a university degree? Even the school teachers have had only two years of normal school and whenever one of our own children, I mean those of other parents, gets through high school they leave immediately to get jobs Down Below. Yes, there are times when I hunger to talk with a person of some education. Imagine having a real University professor at our dinner table!"

Arriving on the morning train, Professor Johnson got a ride up our long him street with Mr. Marchand, our mail carrier. He told us later that he and Marchand had talked French all the way up to our house. He was fascinated by the differences in pronunciation, he said. "M'sieur Marchand speaks a patois that is the French of three hundred years ago. That would make a good study all by itself."

Dad was away making house calls but mother made him welcome with coffee, toast and wild strawberry jam. I almost laughed when I saw him with his hat off. A little old man with a forehead that ran up over and behind his head and with a little pointed white beard, he looked more like a merry old elf than a scholar. When Mother took him upstairs I tried to bring up his suitcase but he took it away from me. "It's too heavy," he said. "I have a lot of books in it, mainly books about Finland and the Finnish language about which I know little. I understand, Mrs. Gage, that there is a substantial population of Finns and their offspring in this locality?"

"Yes," Mother replied. "More than half of us are Finns; perhaps a quarter are French Canadians and the rest are Cousin Jacks, Scandinavians, Indians and other assorted nationalities."

"Cousin Jacks?" he inquired.

"Oh, that's what we call the people who worked the tin mines in Cornwall, England, and emigrated to the U.P." Then Mother showed him Grandma's room. "This black walnut furniture was my mother-in-law's," she said. "She lived with us until she died. It's very old and very old fashioned. See the marble tops on the dresser and table and the carvings."

"It's beautiful," the Professor commented, running his hands over the gleaming wood. "And look at this escritoire desk with the built-in book shelves. A fine place to do my transcribing." He took down one of the volumes from the shelves, *The Memoirs of Ulysses S. Grant.*

"Yes," Mother said. "Most of those books are about the Civil War. My father-in-law, Grampa Van, fought in the Battle of Shiloh and was taken prisoner. Grandma Van had a pension."

"I'm a fortunate man, Mrs. Gage. I can't tell you how much I appreciate your hospitality. What a lovely room!"

"I'll leave you now to get organized," Mother said. "My husband will be back for dinner in about an hour, so come down whenever you're ready."

I don't remember too much about the conversation that noon and a lot of it I didn't understand, but the Professor described the work of a linguistic scholar and how he practiced it. "We dissect languages just as you dissected your cadavers, Doctor," he said. "We identify the surface features such as pronunciation and also the deep structures such as grammar - first the skin of the language and then the bones and muscles. We analyze how they fit together, determine their functions." There was more but I got to thinking about how Mullu or Fisheye and I would be going fishing that afternoon when what he was saying got my attention.

"First I have to get a corpus, a representative collection of utterances spoken by the native speakers."

"You'd better not call them natives," Dad interjected. "They'll resent it."

"Yes, yes, I know. And then I transcribe those utterances into the International Phonetic Alphabet. I've trained myself to do what we call shadowing - covertly saying to myself the words the other person is speaking. If he says 'Don't', I silently say 'don't' just as he said it, perhaps like this: 'Don't (don't) tell (tell), your (your) mother. Then I try to echo the whole utterance to myself exactly as spoken, and finally I write it down in this new alphabet. Would you like to see it, Doctor? I have it upstairs."

He brought down two copies, one for each of my parents, and I looked at it over my Mother's shoulder as the professor explained. "English is a very unphonetic language," he said, "and the letters used in spelling it often do not represent the actual sounds. For example, we use the *t* and the *h* to spell the word "think" but the sound has neither a *t* nor an *h* in it. Therefore, to accurately transcribe the actual sound we use the symbol 'θ. You'll observe that many of the symbols in this alphabet are like those of our ordinary alphabet but there are new ones we've had to

invent. Let me transcribe what I've just said so you can understand."
He did so.

"That's very interesting," Mother commented, "but I've noticed that a lot of our people also omit a lot of the words as in saying "You go store and buy meat, eh?""

"That's interesting too," replied the Professor. "So they omit prepositions and articles and end the sentence with a rising inflection? The latter suggests some Swedish influence or perhaps Finnish. Oh, I can hardly wait to get started collecting. I feel like a puppy with a new bone." His little goatee waggled with enthusiasm. "Have you any suggestions, Doctor, about where I could begin to get my specimens?"

Dad gave it some thought. "Well, you can't just go up to a door and ask for conversation," he said, "and if you try to explain what you're trying to do, they'll be offended or think you're crazy. They think they talk all right, and besides most of them are suspicious of strangers. No, you'll have to eavesdrop at first until you can establish some contacts. Let's see..."

After a pause to full his pipe Dad continued. "I guess the best spots to do your collecting of specimens would be at Higley's saloon, the railroad depot, the post office, the barber shop and Flynn's store. I'll have Cully show you where they are and he can tell you about our village at the same time." My face fell. There went my afternoon's fishing!

The only person we met on our way uptown was Reino Okanen. "Hey, Cully," he said. "I yust seen Mullu. He look for you, I tink. Say you going fis-sing, mebbe so, eh?"

As we passed on, I heard the Professor say just what Reino had said and it was uncanny. He had the same voice and words and tones. He stopped right there on the sidewalk, pulled out a notebook and fountain pen, and began scribbling and muttering to himself as he did so. "Yust" for "just"; "seen" for "saw"; omitted "is"; substituted *t* for *th* in think; omitted pronoun "he"; used "say" for "said"; omitted "plan to"; substituted *s* for *sh* in fishing and split the syllables (fiss-sing); oh yes, and again the Scandinavian upward inflection at the end of the utterance." Lord, the old professor was sure excited. "Cully," he exclaimed. "Marvellous, marvellous! A genuine dialect for sure. But do others talk like that young man?"

I grinned, "Ya, I tink so," I said. "Ve all got goot U.P. brogue for talk ourself - but not for home or school, no."

When we reached Flynn's store, I told him it would usually be a good place to collect samples, that people liked to wander around looking for stuff and to talk to each other, but when we entered we were the only ones inside. "Maybe you'd like to buy me a little bag of candy" I suggested. "Olga, who'll wait on us, talks U.P. good." If I couldn't go fishing I could salvage something from the lost afternoon.

Olga did wait on us. "Vat kine candy you vant?" she asked the professor. He turned to me. "What kind would you like, Cully?" he asked.

Olga horned in. "Ve got gudt socolates wit tzerries in dem. Or dis box taffy, maybe so?" I said I'd just like some of the big round jawbreakers because they lasted so long. Olga was disappointed but she said tanks anyway. When we were leaving I noticed that old lady Terrance was in the meat market, so I nudged the professor to go in there with me. "I'll be 'aving some of they cheese, Mr. Ryan," she said to the butcher. "But if ye don't mind would ye cut me an 'alf (half) pound with they 'am knife. I dearly love they taste of 'am (ham)."

"Let's sit a bit on the fence railing, Cully," the professor said after we left the store. Again he mimicked both Olga and the old Cornish woman as he wrote in his notebook. "Incredible!" he said. "The melting pot indeed. I've found the mother lode in Tioga." I told him about the Cornish and their pasties and saffron bread and how they always said "they" for "the", and dropped their *h's* on some words while inserting them in others where they didn't belong. He complimented me for my keen observation and said perhaps I'd become a linguist too when I grew up. "No!" I answered. "I'm going to be a lumberjack."

Dad had suggested the barber shop and post office. We didn't enter the former. "There's no point going in there now," I told the professor. "Wait until evening when the men go there after work to play pool. Buy some soda pop and peanuts and just sit there listening. You'll hear plenty. Then I told him about Annie, our postmistress. Her folks had come from Sweden but though she'd been born in this country and gone to school in Tioga, her speech still had a lot of the flavor of the language her family had always spoken at home. I imitated how the last words of her sentences always rose in pitch. "Just introduce yourself, say you're staying with us and may be expecting some mail," I told him. "Annie knows almost everything that goes on in town," I said, "almost as much as Aunt Lizzie. She'll be asking you a lot of questions, so be prepared. But don't tell her why you're here or everyone in town will know and then they might not talk to you. Just ask her what sights you ought to see." Annie sure told him, a half hour's worth, and the professor was mopping his brow when we left.

"I think I'd better go back to your home now, Cully. My brain is reeling and I've got to get my transcription done right away." I asked him if he didn't want to go downtown to the saloon and railroad station as Dad had suggested and he said yes but that he'd like to have an hour at home first to rest and think.

Mother gave the professor some tea and cookies when he came downstairs and then he was ready to go again. Down the hill we went, past Old Blue Ball's house and the school and the three churches, and I'd just pointed out Callahan's store as a good place to collect samples when we met Fisheye, one of my two best friends. "Me, I was just coming up see you, Cully," he said after I'd introduced them to each other. "Eef I stay 'ome my mudder fine me work for to do." Out of the corner of my eye I could see the professor's lips moving silently. For the first time I noticed Fisheye's accent and speech. I'd never been aware that it was any different from my own.

"Come along with us, Fisheye," I suggested. "The professor wants to know where the depot and saloon are. He's staying at our house and I'm to show him the town, what there is of it."

After seeing the depot and the saloon, Fisheye said, "I tink your fren like to see old fur-nace (he accented the second syllable) and ze waterfall, yes? My granpere, he haul ze stone for eet long time 'go. Ze waterfall, she is tirty feet high. Dey use zee wa-ter (again accenting the second syllable) for to cool peeg iron zat zey smelt dere in fur-nace. Yes." The professor admired the cascading water and the ruins of the old furnace but when he took out his notebook and began writing in it, Fisheye was curious. The professor turned over a page and rapidly drew a sketch of the furnace with the water flowing over the cliff behind it. "I like to remember and these notes and sketches help me," he said. He showed us the picture and it was very good. "Me, I nevair see artiste before," Fisheye exclaimed.

Just before we dropped off Fisheye Dr. Johnson asked about the blacksmith's shop and why there was a huge iron triangle hanging from the roof peak. "Oh, dat's Paddy Feeny's gong," Fisheye said. "Paddy, he bang dat for Saint Patrick's day ever year, yes. He Irish." I thought of going in so the professor could hear him talk but Paddy was busy. Paddy had a fine brogue, I told Mr. Johnson, and there were several other Irish families in town. Katy Flanagan's kids talked just like Paddy did.

That evening after supper the professor summarized his findings of the day to my interested parents. "Cully was a great help," he said. "I know where to collect my corpus of samples and have already got enough to convince me that there is indeed a U.P. dialect. It seems mainly to reflect two languages, French and Finnish, but other languages too have had their influence. Perhaps the most prevalent phonetic feature is the use of *t* and *d* for our two *th* sounds. They say 'dese, dose, and dem' for 'these, those and them',and they say 'tink' for 'think', 'tirsty' for 'thirsty'. That makes sense because neither Finnish nor French has a *th* sound."

"Yes," Mother interrupted. "I've had to get after Cully for saying 'duh' for 'the' and 'dat' for 'that'. He knows better but that's what he hears all the time."

"The people with whom I talked also seem to use the *s* for the *sh* fairly consistently," the professor continued. "That must be the Finnish influence because the French have a lot of *sh* words such as 'cherie' and 'chef'." He looked in his notebook. "Yes," he said, "I've heard 'wassing' for 'washing' and Annie, your postmistress, told Cully to be sure to 'sut the door'."

53

"I'll watch for that in Cully's speech," Mother interjected.

"Similarly, your people seem to substitute the 'y' for the voiced affricate 'j'. They say 'yump' for 'jump' and 'Yanuary' for 'January'. They use *v* for the *w* and *wh* sounds: 'vant' for 'want' and 'Vere you going, Cully?' for 'Where are you going?' "

Again he referred to his notebook. "Oh yes, many voiced sounds are unvoiced. They say 'poy' for 'boy' and 'iss' for 'is'. Oh, I've just begun to scratch the surface."

"You really can dissect the language," Dad said, admiringly.

"And then there are the vowel differences too. Cully's friend Fisheye nasalized a lot of them as the French do, but very frequently all of the speakers tended to use the short vowel 'eh' for the 'a' as in 'sat' or 'catch'. They say 'set' and 'ketch'! And then there's curious prolonging of vowels that may have a Finnish origin."

"Yes," said my father. "You'll hear them say 'Saatana' for Satan and 'puuko' for knife." There was more of the same but I went to bed early.

The next day Professor Johnson was bubbling with enthusiasm when we assembled for dinner. "I started at the post office as the mail was being distributed. 'Disturbed', they call it. As we waited, one woman approached me. 'You stay Doctor's house, eh? He fine man. You go fis-sing, maybe so? Doctor, he goodt fisserman.' I told her I hoped to although I've never fished in my whole life. But we had quite a conversation."

"Yes," Mother said, "the whole town knows you're here and are curious. Did you tell her of your project?"

"No, I was afraid it might stop her from talking."

"If it was Mrs. Erickson as I suspect, you didn't need to worry" said Mother, "but did you make any new discoveries?"

"Oh yes, indeed," replied the professor. "I'm coming to believe that a dominant feature of this dialect is the way the people handle the language itself. They omit many words, the articles and prepositions, mainly. They say, 'Go store?' for 'Are you going to the store?' Yes, and they often omit such auxiliary verbs as 'is' and 'are'. And oh, the double negatives that I hear everywhere! I was down in Callahan's store listening to two old codgers talking about 'deer hun-ting' and one said, 'Duh secon' veek in deer camp vee nevair soot no deer.', that sort of thing."

He turned to Dad. "Doctor," he said', "One of the problems I'm facing is determining the consistency of their utterances. Hearing snatches of conversation isn't enough. I need to have an opportunity to analyze the speech of just one person over a longer period of time. Have you any suggestions?"

Dad thought for a moment. "Yes," he said. "I think I could arrange to have Arvid Makela take you fishing, trolling for northern pike in our big lake. That way you'd be with him for an extended time for sample collecting, and besides you should see our lovely Lake Tioga with its islands. If you'd pay him five dollars for being your guide, he'll be your friend forever. I understand he's out of work now and he has a boat down there."

The professor responded enthusiastically. "Wonderful!" he said. "I've wanted to go fishing all my life and never had a chance to do so. That sounds perfect. But is Mr. Makela a second generation Finn? I can't have my data corrupted by having samples from those who have just immigrated."

"Yes," Dad replied. "It was Arvid's grandfather who came over from the old country. I don't think the Makelas even speak Finnish in their home now, though he sure has a pronounced accent. How about tomorrow afternoon and evening? Edyth will fix you a snack if you miss supper. The fish bite better along toward sundown." The professor greeted the suggestion eagerly.

At suppertime Mr. Johnson told us of a new discovery. "Over and over again I've heard a language usage that comes directly from the French," he said. "Your people often insert a pronoun after a subject noun. Here are some samples." He pulled out his notebook. "'Me, *I* go store now,' 'That old fart Slimber, *he* best liar in town,' 'My cow, *she* no give much milk now.' And there's another feature too that is common in French and your U.P. dialect: the final sounds are omitted or formed in the mouth but not spoken. 'Ole (old) man Viirta;' 'You get da verm (worms);' 'He dohn (don't) do nuttin but sit on ass alla time.' Oh, there were many other specimens of the same kind. I'm just fascinated." He spent the morning wandering around town and the early part of the afternoon upstairs working on his notes, but had tea with Mother about three o'clock. "Mrs. Gage," he said, after eating one of her big sugar cookies, "Have you noticed that the people up here often accent the wrong syllable? Not that it's wrong - just different."

"What do you mean?" asked Mother. "Can you give me an example?"

Well, they say 'DEE-troit', not Detroit, and I've heard such locutions as 'ba-CON, om-LET, on-YAN' for 'onion,' and 'pota-TOES'. "

"Oh, that's how the French Canadians talk," said Mother. Changing the subject, she asked him a few personal questions. Was he married? He told her no, that being a scholar was a lonely life, that, except for his travels, he'd spent most of it in books and classrooms and his study. "Now that I'm almost sixty-five, Mrs. Gage, I know how much I've missed, but I guess it's too late to do anything about it now."

I overslept next morning and just got in on the tail end of the professor's report of his experiences in the barber shop and saloon. "The young man and I had a pleasant little conversation about the weather in winter. 'Many times it go tirty peeloh and more. Lotsa snow. Vee go ski and snowshoe over drift up to ear, yah.' That sounded as though he were of Finnish ancestry so I asked him from whence his forebears had come. For some reason that seemed to irritate the man 'Vatcha mean? I no got four bears, no got one even. You talk funny,

Mister. Vere you from? You salesman, eh?' When I told him I was from Ann Arbor, he said, 'Oh, you be anudder bastard from Down Pelow.' and that was the end of the conversation."

"You can't use academic language like that," Dad commented. "You're lucky you didn't get a punch in the nose. We're proud people up here. Oh by the way, I've made the arrangements and Arvid Makela will come by about three o'clock to take you fishing. Don't forget to pay him. And don't overpay him either if you want to preserve your nose."

Just before I went to bed the professor came to the back door lugging a huge pike, perhaps ten pounds or more. His face was beaming. "I've never had so much fun in my life, Doctor," he said. "Arvid caught three and I caught this one. He cleaned and scaled it too. Would it be possible that Mrs. Gage might cook it tomorrow?"

"Of course, I will," said Mother. "My husband doesn't particularly care for pike because of the forked bones but he'll eat it and I'd welcome a change from the brook trout he's always bringing home."

"What a lovely lake you have. All those islands. And crystal clear water and the trees, birch, huge maples and pines. I've never seen such a beautiful place. Indeed, I almost forgot my mission but I've got a notebook full of Arvid's talk. Good talk too. He's quite a man! Oh, I'm so tired and happy, Mrs. Gage, I think I'll skip having anything to eat and just go to bed."

The rest of the week went by swiftly. Fisheye took him trout fishing twice. Mullu took him to Fish Lake and the cave-in at the old mine. The professor spent one whole day riding in a buckboard with Slimber Vester as old Maude, Mr. Marchand's horse, pulled them up the river road to the old Haysheds logging dam. Of course by that time the whole village knew why he was in Tioga. He was there to study how they talked. He was a professor from some big university Down Below and they felt flattered by his interest. So they made him welcome and talked to him every time they could manage it. If he was Dr. Gage's house guest he must be all right. Completely unconscious of their own speech, they were fascinated by his two pound words, as they called them. They also thought he was a bit crazy but that was OK in Tioga. We had always had our share of nuts and always enjoyed them and their doings. Something to talk about!

Before Professor Johnson left for Ann Arbor he took the train to Ishpeming, returning with a dozen yellow roses for Mother and a big box of El Perfecto cigars for Dad, the best they had in Toutloff's Drug Store.

"I just can't tell you how much I've appreciated being in your home and village," he said to my parents. "I've never, never known such wonderful people or had such a fine time. While I've only got a nucleus of the data I need on the U.P. dialect, I've made a good start and plan to return soon for a more extended stay. Moreover, I've persuaded the Widow Johnson to take me on as a boarder and roomer so I won't have to impose on your incredibly gracious hospitality. Who knows? Perhaps I'll stay here the rest of my life, collecting linguistic samples for a book. And experiencing all the things I've missed."

To know what happened, thereafter, you'll have to translate.

ðə profesɚ dɪd kʌm bæk tu tɑɹogə hwer hi

merid hɪz lændledi ðə wɪdo ænd et hɚ

pæstiz ænd ðə frʃ hi kɔt ænd ðə dɪr hi

ʃɔt ænd bɪkɔz hi hæd pʊt so mʌtʃ ʌv aɹr

spitʃ ɪn hɪz mauθ kəlɛktɪŋ sæmplz hi

endɪd ʌp wɪð ə faɪn juˈpi æksɛnt tu

THE PEACEFUL LITTLE VILLAGE OF TIOGA

In these North-woods Readers I have tried to describe and perhaps pre-serve the culture of Tioga and the U.P. as it was in the early days of this century. Culture hell! We weren't cultured; we were tough and rough and rude and crude. We almost had to be to survive! Our men lived in danger most of their lives getting the iron ore out of the bowels of the earth, felling the great white pines and riding the logs down turbulent, roaring streams at breakup. Our women grew old and bent before their time, washing, ironing, canning without any of today's conveniences and also raising huge hordes of children. The harsh climate with its nine months of bitter winter and three months of poor sledding demanded of all of us the courageous endurance that the Finns called *sisu*. Isolated in the ever encroaching dark forest, we made the best of it and despite everything lived surprisingly happy lives.

From the very beginning we kids in Tioga were taught by precept and example to be tough, to endure pain, punishment, and drudgery. At three, the Finn boys were getting boiled and roasted (broasted) in the sauna once or twice a week. At four, the French Canadian children were hoeing and weeding the potato patch. At five, when I slipped on some rocks and badly bruised and scraped my leg from stem to stern, my father looked it over. "Nothing's broken. Stop your bawling!" he said contemptuously. No matter what happened we weren't supposed to cry. "Crybaby! Crybaby!" That taunt soon taught us not to.

We also taught ourselves to be tough. Pulling our heavy sleds up the mile-long, very steep hill street was very hard when you were only half-past six and your feet and hands seemed frozen but you didn't dare stop to rest lest some other kid come along to yell "Kindergarten Baby, Slopped in the gravy!" In June we'd bare our wrists and let a big mosquito gorge on it until it was finally full enough to swat. The boy with the biggest blood spot was the winner. In April or May when the crows had come back but there was only a ring of black water around the giant ice cake in the middle of Fish Lake, we had to jump into the icy fire and see how long we could bear it. Barefoot in July we'd climb the big cinder pile at the mine until our soles were bleeding and burning in the hot sun. At ten, playing Nosey Poker in the haymow, we did our utmost to restrain our tears when we lost. I should explain that the person with the lowest draw poker hand got ten swats across the tip of the nose with the cards held by each of the other players. We had no money to play with so we didn't bet, but that penalty kept the game interesting if hazardous to the health. Mullu found a magneto from an old Model-T Ford and rigged up a crank so it would give a good shock if you held the terminal wires. The faster you cranked the contraption, the worse the shock. It was murder but we had to see who could endure it the longest. Kids had to be tough in Tioga!

The ability to bear pain without crying, however, sometimes presented a problem. I soon learned that when my father was spanking me (Dad called it "thrashing", a more accurate description), that if I bore the beating stoically his walloping would be harder and last longer. I pondered the dilemma and came up with a more or less satisfactory solution. I wouldn't cry but just groan "Oh, oh, oh" piteously and make sure I got the timing right. One day coming home early from his house calls, Dad found me playing cowboy by riding Rosie, our Jersey milk cow, around the barnyard. I knew it wasn't particularly good for the milk production but I liked the way she galloped and bellered. Well, Dad caught me by the scruff of the neck, opened the back gate of the buckboard, put me in it prone, and started whaling me good. The pitiful oh-oh-oh groanings worked fine. Not too bad! Not as bad as when Old Blue Balls, our school superintendent, hit me when we got caught playing hooky at Fish Lake.

This training in the inhibition of emotion had its drawbacks. For example, the outward expression of affection was frowned upon too in Tioga. Although I'm sure that my mother and father loved each other dearly, never once in all those years did I ever see them hug or kiss each other, or even touch each other fondly. That was for the bedroom behind closed doors, I guess. Any display of tenderness in public was never seen in Tioga, except perhaps in a few of the French Canadians when they'd had too much chokecherry wine. It was unmanly, a sign of weakness. In a rough land we had to be tough!

We also had to be fearless. This dubious virtue was instilled in us very early, at least by the time we entered school. To be called a sissy was bad enough; to feel that you were a coward was infinitely worse! Our fathers faced danger every day of their lives in the mines, cutting down those giant trees, or on their traplines. Every week some of them came wounded to our door or were carried into my father's hospital on a stretcher. Scared by a bear raiding our garbage piles, there were occasionally runaways going down our street, the carriages careening wildly from one side to another behind horses mad with terror. At night in the grove behind my father's hospital we heard wolves chasing deer. There were train wrecks. There were explosions in the fields as farmers dynamited the stumps that thwarted their plows. There were gunshot wounds or deaths. Danger was everywhere back then in Tioga but we coped with it. No big deal! Just had to make it through the winter.

It's a wonder any of us kids ever made it to maturity, the risks we took to prove our bravery. We ran along the rails of sharp picket fences; we made our way precariously down the steep slopes of old ore pits; we scaled the sheer faces of granite cliffs. Last summer I visited the locale of a ski run we made in the hilly woods below the west edge of Company Field. Very steep, the trail wove narrowly through the maples, then angled sharply left to avoid a jumbled mess of huge craggy boulders. To make the sudden turn we had to grab a sapling, swing our skis around, and at the precise second let got to continue the descent. If we didn't do it just right, into that mass of sharp rocks we'd go. Insane! Yet we barreled down that trail day after day and no one got hurt.

We were always daring each other. "Bet you're scared to knock down that wasp's nest!" "Bet you ain't got the guts to taste that jack-in-the-pulpit root!" (Unboiled, it tasted like fire as we all knew). "Let's run across the field!" (The field in which Mr. Salo's vicious bull pawed the ground and bellowed.) "Let's go steal some of Chervais' green apples. He just got rock salt in his shotgun."

We rigged up an old cable from the closed mine between two trees and descended down it hand over hand, over a deep gully. We threw rocks at discarded dynamite caps almost hoping they wouldn't go off though some of them did. We'd climb birch or maple saplings to their tops, then kick our legs outward to make them bend to the forest floor. Some of them only bent part way and then we'd have a long drop to the hard ground. After eating a swiped can of pork and beans in our shack in the woods, we'd take a match and set fire to the farts that resulted. Made a clear blue flame! We hunted snakes and snapped their heads off; we trapped skunks; and we played tricks in school that risked Old Blue Balls' Ruler, Hand or Strap. It was the delicious smell of danger that we wanted in our nostrils as we played our versions of Russian Roulette. We weren't cowards. Nosirrie! Sulu wasn't afraid to eat worms; Fisheye would tuck a big bloodsucker between his thumb and forefinger to watch it swell and change color; Mullu would hang from his legs on the high limb of a tree and swing back and forth; and I, well, I did a lot of damfool things too.

We needed all the courage we could develop back then in Tioga because of all the fighting that went on. It was a way of life, almost a cultural mandate. Was it because civilization, a term that hardly fits, had come to the U.P. and our town only thirty years before, when the first iron mines had opened and the pines were logged? Frontiersmen have always had ready fists everywhere. All I know is that I had to fight my way to and from school far too often and most of my classmates had to do the same. At recess there was always a ring of onlookers reveling in watching two kids battling within it, and when one got licked, another ring would soon be formed with another two boys slugging each other. Our daily entertainment!

There were dog fights, cat fights, impromptu rooster fights. We'd put a handful of red pissants on an anthill of black ants to see them battling to the death. In rutting season the bucks clashed antlers in the nearby forest. Growling cub bears cuffed each other in their play. Chipmunks wrestled and bit each other. Often we'd go up to the old mining pit behind Flynn's store that was used as our town's garbage dump, so we could watch the rats committing mayhem on each other.

Our men fought too, though not as often as we kids did. My father, the doctor, always dreaded Saturday night because he knew he'd have to sew up the slashes made by the Finn's long puuko knives. Finns never stabbed when they fought, just sliced enough to leave a reminder. Most of our young men just used their huge fists, grunting and swinging roundhouse blows until the opponent went down cursing his luck. Outside Higley's saloon, or on the platform of the depot, such fights were a common sight. No one ever interfered. They knew that if they did they'd get clobbered by both of the battlers. Once by the depot I saw two tottering old men hitting each other with their canes and when a brakeman tried to intercede they both began beating him.

Girls and women fought too, though more rarely. Compared to the fights between males, however, their battles were much more vicious. They pulled each other's hair and used their fingernails to scratch faces into bloody messes. As they fought, they cried and wept and screamed, whereas most of the battles between men or boys were pretty silent except when a good blow produced an involuntary ow! Moreover, after the scrap, girls and women held a grudge for a long time, whereas we did not.

There were only two unspoken Marquis of Queensberry rules that seemed to govern our schoolyard battles: No fair hitting your opponent when he was on the ground or not looking, and no fair kicking him in the crotch. The first of these was important because when you knew you were licked you could fall to the ground and escape any further punishment.

Neither of these rules held for men. Many of our old lumberjacks had faces full of scars from the boot caulks of ancient enemies who had not only knocked them down but stomped them. As a boy I never witnessed any fights like that but I sure heard a lot of tales of chokings, ear biting, eye gouging, and the like that had occurred when the lumberjacks came out of the woods in the spring to get drunk and tear up the town. Indeed, I once went fishing overnight up at the headwaters of the Tioga River with Nick Maloney who had spent ten years in prison for killing a man with his fists and then stomping him. He sure had some hair-raising tales of fighting there by the night fire but I liked him and he sure knew how to catch brook trout.

Our schoolyard fights were never as brutal nor did they last as long. We tried only to give the other kid a black eye or bloody nose or to make him bawl and cry uncle.

Why did we kids fight? Apart from the tradition, we probably battled because of the frustration we encountered in school, the tough discipline, the feeling of being cooped up. We fought too in the effort to achieve dominance, to move up in the peck order. "I kin lick you!" was a challenge that started many of our altercations. No anger was involved. We just had to be sure we were the better one when it came to fisticuffs. When someone put a chip on his shoulder or spit on your shoes, you had to accept the dare or be despised. Many of our fights, certainly my own, began with being teased unmercifully. "Cully's a stutter-cat; Cully's a stutter-cat; K-K-K-Katy (from the old song) K-K-K-K-Katy." That's all that was needed to set me swinging for blood. Even after I got so I could lick all the kids in my grade and below, the bigger ones would call me those names knowing that I would fight and that they could give me a trimming. Dear old golden school days? Nuts! Dear old bloody school days, they were. I had more black eyes and bloody noses than anyone in our school.

Until Grampa Gage gave me some lessons! Distressed to see my bruises and battle wounds, he bought a pair of boxing gloves and every day we'd go a few rounds. I learned to hit straight, not in semicircles; I learned how to jab repeatedly with my left hand, then use the right to cream my opponent. Best of all, he taught me to duck my head to the side, ward off a blow with my elbow, and to take a hard blow yet continue fighting even harder. That training sure paid off and most of the teasing stopped.

But I should also mention the gang fighting that characterized those early years in Tioga. Gang is the wrong word. We had no gangs in the modern sense of the word but there had always been a keen rivalry between the Up-towners and the Down-towners, between the French-Canadian and Indian kids who lived in the valley and the Finns,

English, Swede and other kinds who lived on top of the hill.

Those battles were fun fights really, not like the one-on-one scraps in the schoolyard. From ten to twenty kids would assemble, make their plans, gather their ammunition and then send word to the other side that at such an hour we'd be ready for them at a certain place. Rarely was the challenge refused. Depending on the season, we'd fight with slingshots, using pebbles or hazelnuts for bullets, or spears made of cattails, or wild cucumbers (those spiny oblong fruits that sure sting when you get one on the neck), or snowballs, or the frozen horse turds which hurt the most.

We'd line up our forces at each end of the little side street just beyond the Methodist Church by Old Blue Balls' house, advance on each other and try to break each others lines into disarray and flight. Each side had a general, tactics and reinforcements but no prisoners were taken. Unlike our solitary fights which were usually silently carried out, these were full of yelling and shouting as we clashed, so much so that sometimes they called Charles Olafson, our town constable, to restore some calm. These were fun fights because we never used our fists and rarely did anyone get seriously hurt. The last and the best of these battles I have described in my tale "Old Blue Balls" in my first Northwoods Reader so I won't repeat it here, except to say that the cow-pasties flew fast and furious and we joined together to chase him back into his house.

So that's the way it was in the peaceful little forest village of Tioga in the early 1900s.

One afterthought: Grampa Gage told me a tale which I've heard several times since and which you may have heard too. A man was going around the corner of great granite hill when suddenly he saw a huge bear coming right toward him. He got out his jackknife and prayed. "Dear Lord," he said. "If you're on the bear's side, make it quick! And if you're on my side, make it quick! But if you're neutral, Lord, you're going to watch the damndest fight you ever did see."

God was always neutral in Tioga.

63

KILLING THREE BIRDS WITH ONE CHEESE

It really was my father's fault. If he hadn't told us why he'd been kicked out of his rooming house when he was in medical school, I never would have thought of the idea.

But I'd better start at the beginning, which was when Dad pushed aside the big wedge of yellow store cheese and roared that he was sick of it. "Edyth," he said to my mother, "How many times have I told you not to buy this miserable stuff? Where's that stinky cheese, the white brick cheese, we used to have?"

"Mr. Flynn doesn't keep it any more," she replied calmly. "I know you like your cheese ripe and strong but I just can't get it in town. Perhaps the next time you go to Ishpeming..."

"No!" Dad interrupted. "I'll stop in this afternoon and tell Flynn I want some better cheese even if he has to go to Wisconsin to get it. Lord, we're the best customer he has and he knows it. It's not right to spoil one of your fine pies with this junk!"

That evening Mother asked him if he'd seen Mr. Flynn and he said yes, he had, that Flynn had told him his supplier didn't make the stinky brick cheese any more, and that no one except the Gages bought it anyway. He did give Dad the address of a firm that made limburger and my father had already ordered five pounds of it by mail.

"Oh no!" my Mother wailed. "Not Limburger. That'll smell up the whole house. It's putrid! I've never tasted it and I don't want to. My father brought some home once when I was a little girl and I still remember that horrid odor."

Dad grinned. "Yes, it's pretty strong, I'll admit. When I was in Medical School in Ann Arbor, all of us students used to eat some on crackers to get the stink of the cadavers we were dissecting out of our nostrils. Not much refrigeration back then and the formaldehyde they used didn't help much either. Sometimes we'd toast a chunk of Limburger over one of the laboratory lamps to cancel the smell of the stiffs when they were hauled out of the cold room. Boy, did that really clear the air - or pollute it even more!"

I was all ears. I liked the tales Dad told of his days in medical school - like the one where he used a human finger for a book mark. That always drove Mother from the table.

"We were always hungry back then," Dad continued, "and often we'd bring back some of the crackers and Limburger to eat at night when we were studying in the rooming house. Not bad, not bad at all, though you couldn't eat much at a time. I admit it did stink up the place and when our landlady came up one night and found us toasting a bit of it over our kerosene lamp, she raised the roof and insisted we leave the next day."

"Don't blame her a bit!" said Mother. "I'll probably chase you out too when that Limburger cheese comes."

It came! When Annie the postmistress handed me the box as I collected our mail she told me to hurry home, that there must be something very dead inside. Yes, it sure stank even through the cardboard. Mother made me put it, not in the pantry, but in the woodshed, and made Dad open the box and cut the slice he wanted for his pie. I had to taste it too, of course, and if I held my nose it wasn't really too bad. Sorta lingered in your mouth and on your hands for hours though.

Well, Dad had his Limburger cheese with his daily pie for a week or two, but I noticed the slices he cut were getting smaller and then the day came when he said, "Well, that's enough Limburger. From now on let's go back to cheddar." He told me to bury the rest of the box in the manure pile.

That happened about the end of October and now it was the end of February, that bad time of the U.P. year - the dog days of winter when everyone had sickened of snow and spring was a million weeks away. It was even bad for us kids, too. Way below zero for a month, it wasn't much fun playing outside and in school it was worse. We were in P.P.

Polson's room for the second year she'd taught us, or rather tyrannized us. Rules, rules, rules! So many of them it wasn't even fun trying to outwit them. Besides Miss Polson always won. And she drove us and drilled us and disciplined us! Who cared about the capital of Patagonia or distinguishing participles from verbs! Who gave a damn if the push-pulls weren't slanted correctly in the ovals of the Palmer writing? None of us did. I didn't! I was bored silly. I'd read all the textbooks three times, had mastered fractions,memorized all the junk I had to and was sick, sick, sick of school. Sometimes in the morning I'd lie a bit longer in bed trying to decide if I'd play sick that day so I could stay home, even though I knew it meant calomel and castor oil. Washington's Birthday, Birthington's Washday, Bleah!

I was also afraid to go to school because of Toivo Maki, the school bully, who I knew would hurt or humiliate me. A big Finn kid, he was, and mean! A really good fighter too, he had even licked some of the high-school boys as well as all of us in the seventh grade. Once, when he was beating on me and Fisheye and Mullu came to my defense, he trimmed the three of us but good. Every day I knew he'd be waiting for me in the morning. "Kiss my ass!" he'd demand and when I wouldn't he'd slug me till I cried. I'd often try to make an excuse so I wouldn't have to go out for recess but that didn't always work, so he'd get me again. At noon it wasn't so bad because I was one of those who went home for lunch and Toivo didn't. He carried his dinner pail, ate in the basement and tortured other kids till the bell rang and he had to go to class. But when school let out Toivo would be ready for me again.

Perhaps nowdays a kid in the same predicament might tell his parents or teachers about a similar situation, but that would have been unthinkable back then in the Tioga of the early nineteen hundreds. My father would have told me to fight my own battles and to take my lickings if I had to, that it was character building. As for telling P.P. Polson, why I would have been ostracized by the other kids from then on! So instead, up there in bed each morning I fantasized. I'd put that Toivo in a cage with some big rats and let them eat him as I gloated. That sort of thing. But one morning in bed I had an idea about revenge that shocked me, it was so perfect. Why I could kill three birds with one stone: get even with Toivo, play a good trick on P.P. Polson, and maybe even succeed in getting school dismissed! The enormity of it made me shiver. But did I have the guts to carry it out?

No, I decided, but Fisheye might. Fisheye wasn't afraid of anything, and if his folks found out they wouldn't give a damn. Fisheye was the oldest of nine children and slept in the cowbarn at night because there was no room for him in the house. Yes, he'd go for it. If he got caught and Old Blue Balls gave him The Strap, well, he'd had it before and survived. My friend had known beatings both at school and at home all his life so the prospect of one more wouldn't faze him.

Like Toivo, Fisheye didn't go home for lunch because he lived way down in the valley and there had been many times when he came to school with no lunch at all. When I told my mother about it, she told me that when that happened I was always to bring him home to eat with us, and he had often done so.

That morning I had a hard time concentrating in school and had my ears pulled and felt Miss Polson's ruler twice, so intent I was in the planning. I'd bring Fisheye home at noon and after we'd eaten we'd get that Limburger cheese out of the manure pile, take it to the classroom and he'd sneak in and put it on the steam radiator and...and...and...And all hell would break loose!

Coming home with Fisheye that noon, I explained my plan and he was entranced. "That's a good one," he said. "That's a dandy!" We ate hurriedly, then went to the barn where I got a pitchfork to unearth the Limburger box. It took some work because the manure pile was pretty frozen but that was good because when we found it the cheese had frozen too and stank more of manure than anything else, but I knew that when it thawed under the steam radiator it would smell plenty. Indeed it was so frozen I had to chop it with an axe to break off a big piece and a little one and put them in a brown store bag I'd already hidden in the barn. "Just tuck it behind and under the radiator bag and all," I told Fisheye. "There's lots of bags like that and nobody will know where it came from. A lot of kids bring their lunches in them."

We hurried back to school, getting there about twenty minutes before the bell was to ring. I should explain that at noon all the classrooms were empty and no pupil was to go back to his room until the bell rang. We either had to play outside or, in the winter months, play in the basement gym where the kids ate their lunches under the supervision of one of the teachers. We knew that P.P. Polson, had that supervising duty that month so she wouldn't be in our classroom. Nevertheless, we were plenty scared as Fisheye did his dirty work while I watched outside the door in case someone did come by.

It didn't take long, so Fisheye and I went down to the basement to join the other kids until the bell rang. Toivo was there, of course, hogging the basketball so others couldn't have a turn shooting it. I winked at Fisheye and whispered, "He's got a surprise coming!"

Finally the bell rang and all of us ascended the stairs to our classrooms. "Quiet, children," P.P. said, "Quiet! We will have five minutes of quiet before we begin!" Fisheye and I looked across at each other. We couldn't smell a damned thing.

The wall clock said one-thirty before we got the first whiff of the thawing Limburger, but by one-forty-five it was coming on loud and clear. Eva Thompson raised her hand. "Miss Polson, please, Howard smells awful bad." Howard (Mule) Cardinal's seat was next to the radiator. "Aw, shut up," he said. "Every fox smells his own hole first." Miss Polson came down and sniffed. "You're right!" she said. "Howard, you go immediately to the bathroom and wash thoroughly and if your shoes smell of manure, wash them too." I didn't dare look at Fisheye.

Within minutes, however, it was certain that the smell wasn't coming from Howard and that it wasn't manure either. That cheese had sure ripened in that manure pile those four months. Wow! What a stink of stinks! The kids first began holding their noses, then began choking. Some of the girls began to cry. Even Miss Polson couldn't stand it. "Children," she screamed over the tumult. "Leave the room. Go to the hall outside and stay there until I get Mr. Donegal and find out what's wrong. And be quiet!"

Down came Old Blue Balls taking two steps at a time, with P.P. following to enter the room. Quiet? You could have heard a pin drop there in the hall. Finally, out he came with the brown paper bag and a sticky mess in his hands. Oh how he glared at us. "I'll find out who did this dirty trick if it takes me a month, and I'll tan his hide so he won't be able to sit down for two!" he roared. Wow, was he mad! Fisheye rolled his eyeballs up into his head and I almost filled my pants. "You children stay right here in the hall until I get rid of this and come back, and Miss Polson, you open all the windows wide," he ordered.

The putrid smell of that Limburger had begun to seep into the hall when Old Blue Balls returned. "Line up along the wall and hold out your hands," he commanded. "There's no danger, but one of you put some Limburger cheese on the steam radiator and I'm going to find out who it was. Then he went down the line, sniffing the hands of every one of us. Lord, how I hoped my own hands didn't smell though I couldn't see how they could, the cheese having been frozen so hard. It was difficult to keep them from trembling but I did, and he passed on. He seemed to linger a bit longer when he came to Howard, perhaps because he'd been closest to it, and did so again when he came to Fisheye, perhaps because he always had a barn smell, sleeping there with the cow as he always had to, but finally he passed on and it was obvious that he hadn't found his quarry.

Old Blue Balls then turned to P.P. "Miss Polson, which of these pupils has been to the bathroom to wash their hands?" he demanded. She told him she didn't know of any. "Well, then, I'll have to examine their coats and mittens," he said. "Whoever carried that damned cheese in here must have left some smell somewhere." He disappeared into the cloakroom. Fisheye and I raised our eyebrows at each other. Then we heard a terrible roar and out Blue Balls stormed, waving a jacket. "Whose coat is this?" he yelled. "It's Toivo's," several kids shouted. "It's Toivo's." Old Blue Balls didn't waste a minute. He grabbed Toivo by the hair and dragged him screaming up the stairs to his office. Pow! Pow! Pow! Oh, how Toivo yelled as The Hand and The Strap walloped him. You could hear him hollering all over the school. "We'll dismiss the class for the rest of the day, children," Miss Polson said. "I trust you have learned that it is unwise to play such an abominable trick. It wasn't funny at all."

Three birds with one stone! I went home pretty happy for once and glad that I had told Fisheye to put the small hunk of the Limburger in Toivo's jacket.

SMOKE RINGS

Occasionally there were times when I begged my Grampa Gage to tell me another story and he would say, "No, Mr. McGillicuddy. I'm not in the mood." He'd talk about other things but no amount of coaxing could sway him. I didn't understand that then but I do now for, as of this moment, I'm not in the mood either. No more tales of the U.P. tonight, my friends!

So let me ramble instead about pipe smoking, a messy habit that I have loved for most of my many years. The first pipe I smoked was an ancient black corncob owned by an old French Canadian named Dick DeGon. He'd seen my friend Rudy and me trying to roll dead leaves into cigars when we were only six years old. "Non, non,! mes amis," he said. "Zat no good for to smoke. I geeve you good smoke, oui!" He filled his black corncob with Peerless tobacco, lit it, and handed it to us. It was awful but we kept taking turns, pretending to be tough big men, until nausea overwhelmed us. How the old Frenchman laughed when we dizzily staggered away. "Me, I teach you good lesson, I tink," he said.

That lesson lasted until I was about eleven or twelve when Mullu had swiped some cigarette papers and tobacco from his father and we smoked them down at our shack in Beaverdam swamp. We didn't get sick that time for some reason but the experience was not a pleasant one. About that same year Fisheye and I made little pipes from acorns by removing their caps, taking out the kernel, and boring a hole at the base into which we inserted straws. They weren't too satisfactory because the straws usually collapsed after two or three puffs and Dad's Granger tobacco was terribly strong.

In high school most of us tried to chew snuff or Redman plug tobacco, but I could never manage them. They tasted awful and the taste lingered for hours in my mouth. I also swallowed some juice once and that was the end of that. Once I tried a cigarette, a "coffin nail", as we called them back then, but I didn't like it either. Indeed, I've never smoked cigarettes in all my life and that perhaps is probably why I've lived so long. In college, in an effort to appear sophisticated, during my freshman year, I did smoke cigars for a short time, mainly long black stogies, but there's nothing so foul as a dead cigar butt, so I quit.

It was in my senior year at the University of Michigan that I really began to smoke a pipe, and I probably never would have done so had I not finished an unfinished song in one of Chaucer's works. Professor Sanford, a world-famous scholar who had written many books on Chaucer and the old English ballads and Keats, taught one class a semester in Chaucer and somehow I managed to get into it. One of the best teachers I have ever known, he made the subject so fascinating I looked forward to each class with great excitement. One day he read to us, using the old English pronunciation, two songs of Chaucer that had been left unfinished in the text, and expressed great regret that the remaining lines had been lost forever. So that evening I finished the songs as I thought they might have ended using all the quaint words and spellings current at Chaucer's time. It was a tricky business getting the verses to rhyme so I worked all night on the task, then early next morning slipped the completed songs under the professor's office door. I did not sign my name.

Well, when I came to his class that afternoon, I found that Dr. Sanford had written the two songs on the blackboard along with my additional verses. He said he was utterly delighted, that there were only a few mistakes which he pointed out, and then he asked the student who had written them to see him after class. Too shy, and fearing that my stuttering would make the situation uncomfortable for both of us, I did not accept the invitation, hating myself for not doing so. He was not to be deterred, however, and by having us write something in class so he could identify the handwriting, he insisted that I come with him to his office for afternoon tea and so he could know me better.

That was the beginning of a wonderful treasured experience. Professor Sanford took me under his wing, made me his assistant, shared with me his great learning and wisdom, and became my friend and model. He read all the stuff I'd been writing and encouraged me to write more. With his considerable influence he opened many doors that had been closed to me, arranging to let me have access to the library's stacks and rare book room, and gave me tickets to symphonic concerts, plays, and art exhibitions. Through him I met many of the famous poets and writers of the time. He was my mentor and I was his protege.

I was also his errand boy, getting the books he wanted, abstracting articles, occasionally correcting student papers, and even buying him shoestrings and tobacco. Not any old kind of tobacco either; it had to be Serene Mixture. The professor was a pipe smoker. In his office, lined with books from ceiling to floor, a halo of pipe smoke always hung over his head. On his desk was a large pipe rack, the holes holding at least ten or eleven briar pipes of various sizes and shapes. Each one of them had a name but I can only recall Aristophanes and Marcus Aurelius, his favorites. Never did he smoke the same pipe again on a single day. "That's the only way to keep them sweet, Cully," he told me. "Any fool who keeps smoking the same pipe all day will have a raw tongue and a bad pipe too." Nor did he ever return one to its rack without running a pipe cleaner through it.

One day, after I'd deposited a royalty check for him at the bank, he gave me a twenty dollar bill which back then had the same purchasing power as a hundred dollar bill would now. "I want you to go to the tobacconist and buy a pipe for me, please," he said. When I protested that I wouldn't know a good one from a bad one, he grinned and said, "Well, I'll tell you. Buy one that looks a bit like Marcus Aurelius here: straight stem but slightly curved at the mouthpiece, not too long, and be sure the rim of the bowl is about a quarter of an inch wide. Thin bowls never get a good cake. Try to get one with briar that is straight-grained and with no signs of knots or flaws. See if it fits lovingly between the thumb and forefingers and shake it by the tip to be sure it isn't top heavy."

I sure didn't relish the assignment and when I returned I was very apprehensive as I handed him the case and his change. Dr. Sanford opened it, took out the pipe and examined it for a long time before he spoke. "A good one," he said. "I couldn't have selected a better one myself. With the proper breaking in, it will be a comfort to you all your life." Noticing my incredulous expression, the old man smiled. "Yes, Cully, this pipe is yours. Please accept it as a token of my appreciation for all the help you've given me - and for your companionship too." I was so overcome by the gift I incoherently stammered my thanks and fled from his office.

The next afternoon when I stopped by to see if he had anything he wanted me to do, I found Professor Sanford and another man playing guitars and singing, having a high old time. "This is Carl Sandburg, Cully," he said, "and we're comparing his Appalachian collection of old English songs with those I've unearthed from Elizabethan times. If you want to, just sit in the corner and listen." I did so and it was one of the best afternoons in my life. Carl Sandburg was one of the most prominent poets in America at that time. You probably know his poem about Chicago or the line about how the fog came in on little cat feet. Anyway, they ignored me from that time on and had a ball, but I've never forgotten it.

Dr. Sandford (a lonely man, whose wife had died a few years before,) always was in his office until midnight so, the evening I dropped in again to see him and to express my appreciation. "I'm glad you came, Cully," he said. "Do you have your pipe with you? I want to show you how to break it in."

I had purchased a pouch of Sir Walter Raleigh smoking tobacco but had not yet tried the pipe. The Professor approved of my choice. "It's a very mild tobacco," he said, "a fine one to use at first. You may want to have a stronger kind later."

Then he showed me how to fill it just one small layer at a time and each one lovingly tamped down before the next layer was added. "Tuck it down around the edges with your forefinger so it's firm but not hard," he said. "For the first month or so, never fill it more than half way to the rim and smoke all of it before refilling. That way you'll establish a fine-grained cake all around the inside of the bowl. Some benighted souls smear the inside of the bowl first with honey because it makes a cake swiftly, but I never do. Honey makes for a coarse cake, one that will not absorb the tobacco tars as well." He handed me a bunch of kitchen matches. "These work best," he said. "They hold a flame longer. Just don't scratch them on your pants or they'll leave a mark." He showed me how to twirl the match just after lighting it so the flame would be a steady one and to hold it just above the tobacco until all the surface was ignited. "Take little short puffs," he insisted, "but slow, not fast ones. Never inhale or blow smoke out of your nostrils. Just hold it in your mouth and then let it come out slowly and gracefully. Most of the pleasure of pipe smoking is visual, as you'll find if you try to smoke in the dark." Oh there was a lot more, but I've forgotten.

That happened sixty-three years ago and I've been a pipe smoker ever since. Lord, the pipes I've had and lost and broken and discarded in that time. People keep giving me more of them each year so I always have a-plenty. I've had curved ones, pipes with twelve-inch stems, one made from a calabash gourd, several made of clay. One of the latter that I purchased in Ireland turned out to be an excellent pipe and as it aged it took on a beautiful brown color. A stutterer from Iran named Abdullah sent me a water pipe (a hookah) in appreciation for my successful therapy with him. That hookah was fun to smoke at first. The tobacco bowl sat on a vase of water which in turn sat on the floor at my feet and when I puffed, delightful volleys of filtering bubbles occurred in the vase. Unfortunately, the six-foot pliable rubber stem to my mouth was impossible to clean and soon I could not bear to smoke it. I also have some meerschaum pipes from Turkey that are still virgin, because once when I was a young man I went to a famous pipe shop in Chicago and asked to buy a good meerschaum. The proprietor refused to sell me one. "Nein, nein!" he said, "You are too young. Save something for your old age," and sold me a briar pipe instead. Perhaps in a few more years I'll be old enough to smoke a meerschaum.

I've experimented with many kinds of pipe tobacco too. The aromatic ones smell fine when you open the pouch, but they're too strong for me and I found they soon spoil a good pipe. Once I bought a large set of many different kinds of tobacco from many lands and attempted to design a perfect mixture of my own, only to discover that I couldn't. So I've been smoking Sir Walter Raleigh, the kind I started with, ever since.

Have I become addicted? Oddly, I do not believe so. Certainly not in the physiological sense of an addiction to the nicotine. I never inhale the smoke, just let it linger in the mouth for a bit before slowly blowing it out. For forty years, to make sure, I quit pipe smoking for a month every single year and found it very easy, with no withdrawal symptoms. I just missed the pleasure of the whole process from scratching the match to tapping out the final ashes, but I didn't miss it very much. These last years, however, I've quit trying to build character and so enjoy my pipes all year long.

A psychiatrist told me once that I was a pipe smoker because of an oral fixation on my mother's breast, that I was still an infantile suckling. I didn't tell him that I had been a bottle baby from the beginning because I knew he'd say of course, that I was still trying to make up for my deprivation. If so, so be it! All I know is that it's very comforting to suck sweet lazy smoke from a good pipe.

And my pipes are good ones. I have two sets of them, each with ten pipes in their racks, and not one of them bites. I smoke each set for two weeks, using a different pipe each time and no more than six or seven different ones on a given day. I clean each one with a pipe cleaner after smoking it, and after the two weeks on one set I burn out their stems with a straightened coat hanger heated cherry red before turning to the other set. Many modern pipes have a place in the stem for a filter but I use a twisted pipe cleaner instead which works much better. Sometimes I use my jackknife to scrape an excessive cake from the bowl.

Where and when do I smoke these pipes of mine? When I'm not at my beloved cabins in the U.P. I live in a 130-year-old brick farmhouse on an eighty-acre farm, now surrounded by the city of Portage. Just behind the barns is a four-acre plot that my wife and I long ago turned into a park planted with pines and birch and maple, my miniature U.P. The trees, now forty feet tall, hold a little pool and that is where I have my early morning pipe as I watch the birds and animals coming to drink. We've even had deer.

Behind the garage I have my Secret Garden, so hidden by bushes and tall flowers you wouldn't suspect it was there. A mass of flowers circles a crab apple tree, and in one corner opposite the arbor where I sit is a fountain dancing in a huge cast iron hog-scalding kettle. Overhead are the great branches of burr oak trees, trees that were saplings when the house was built before the Civil War. It's a quiet, lovely spot and there I smoke another pipe midmorning.

After lunch I enjoy still another and different pipe either on the front porch of the old house watching the cars go by the mailbox at the end of the long lawn, or when sitting on the shaded circular bench built around the largest of our great oaks. Then, after a mandatory nap which I still resent, I usually smoke another one in my big chair as I mull over the stuff that should go into a story I'm about to write, but I never smoke while writing or chopping wood or working in my gardens. I save my best pipe for Happy Hour at five and have another one just before I go to bed.

So in a few minutes I will be sitting by a fine black walnut fire blazing in the big fireplace, a very old man in a very old house contentedly smoking a very old pipe named Professor Sanford. I'll blow a smoke ring for you, my friend.

THE SAD SIDE

In my endeavor to portray the life we led in the U.P. during the early part of this century I fear that I may have painted too rosy a picture. Old men seem to remember the funny, happy experiences of their past lives more than the unhappy ones. Tioga had its share of both and so I'm going to try to recall a bit of its sad side.

I. *Mullu*

Some tragedies are major; others are played in a minor key. Let me begin with one of the latter, the tale of how my friend Mullu got his heart broken. As you may recall, he, Fisheye and I were very close friends - the Unholy Trio of Tioga - always getting into one trouble after another, always enjoying each other's company. Unfortunately that relationship began to change when we entered high school, mainly because Mullu had fallen in love. Yes, he had it bad! Why, rather than go swimming with us after school, he'd walk Amy Erickson home carrying her books. Also, on weekends, he was always cutting pulp on his father's forty at five cents a stick. ("A Stick?" A stick was eight feet long and varied in diameter from six inches to a foot. Besides you had to take off the limbs from that spruce or balsam to get that nickle.) Mullu didn't really have to cut the pulp, but he needed money to spend on Amy and to save so he could buy a new suit and shoes. And he was always combing his hair, for Gosh sakes!

Most of our boys had a crush on Amy Erickson — except Fisheye and me. Oh, I'd had one too earlier as my Valentine tale revealed, but, since it got me nowhere I forgot her blonde hair, brown eyes and that crazy giggle. She was pretty, all right, but not as beautiful as a brook trout. Occasionally when she flirted with me as she did with every other boy, I felt good but even better when I could spurn her. As for Fisheye, well he didn't like girls either. Both of us felt badly to see poor Mullu caught in her net.

Things came to a head when the end of May brought the Senior Prom. It wasn't much of a shindig compared to the ones they have now, but it was "big doings" back then. For weeks the girls made their plans. They would put streamers overhead in the gymnasium and have a bower made of fir branches for the Queen. The music would be provided by our little High School makeshift dance band. Not much of a band! I played the saxophone; Mule Cardinal, the trumpet; Fisheye, the school drums, and I forget who had the clarinet and accordion. All of us played by ear and if I recall aright, our repertoire consisted of three different waltzes, two foxtrots, and one polka. That was it! When we played them all we just played them again. Unfortunately when the prom committee heard us rehearse one night after school, they decided not to have us if they could help it. So they made a lot of Prom programs out of flowered wallpaper and sold them for a quarter apiece until they had enough raha to hire a three-piece accordion band from Michigamme.

By this time Mullu had earned enough money to get his new suit and shoes from Sears Roebuck, though his mother had to spend half the night lengthening the sleeves and legs. He also had enough left to buy his program and to persuade Amy to put him down for six of the ten dances. No, he did not ask any other girl to fill in the blank spaces. Holding that brown-eyed blonde in his arms six times would be enough!

Back then no boy ever took his girl to such a dance, though he'd take her home if willing. All the boys went together and stood together in a corner of the hall and the girls did too. Then when the music started and if the boy had the girl's name on his program, he'd go over to her and away they'd go. This system worked well because if, by chance a girl's program was not entirely filled, you could see who was available. Even the plainer ones got picked up.

Mullu's tragedy, as I said, was a minor one - but not to Mullu. Indeed, I don't think he ever got over it. What happened was this. A week before the prom, he noticed a couple of little sores on his left cheek and the next day there were six of them. Then they appeared on his right cheek. Acne! Someone told him to daub carbolic acid salve on them but when he did, they got worse. When he went to school the day before the big night, Amy asked for his program and scratched out her name six times. "You're repulsive, Mullu," she said brutally. "I don't want you near me. Stay home or dance by yourself in the outhouse." A minor tragedy, I suppose, but Mullu never did get married, not to Amy nor to anyone else.

****

II. *Mrs. Beatty*

Mrs. Beatty lived in a little white house about four doors from us. When I was a young boy she was very, very old, just waiting to die, our people said, but they took good care of her. Tioga always took care of its own. The neighbors kept her woodbox filled and brought her berries, apples, and garden produce when they checked up on her. My father, the doctor, paid her a visit each week to listen to her arthritic aches and pains without charging her his usual fee of three dollars for a home call. My mother often dropped in for afternoon tea, though she usually had to make it and pour it because Mrs. Beatty's hands shook so hard. Over and over again she heard the old lady's accounts of her son George's boyhood, the foods he liked, the way she always had to keep his hair combed, the time he found a dozen rotten eggs hidden by a roving hen, his minor escapades. "Jarge is in California now," she'd say, "but I hear from him every Christmas, I do, and sometime he'll be coming home, he will. He's a good boy, Jarge is." Mrs. Beatty lived entirely in the past, and was confused by the present. Often, when I'd go to Flynn's store for her, she'd call me "Jargie-Boy" and give me a brown tart with cinnamon on it as a reward.

One Christmas Mrs. Beatty got a present from her son in California, a large box containing a gramaphone. You may have seen pictures of those early phonographs showing the big fluted wooden horn with a white dog listening to scratchy music coming from the wax cylinders on the box below it. Using the pamphlet of instructions, my father finally managed to assemble it and I was there when he put the needle against the revolving cylinder. Suddenly, we heard Sir Harry Lauder singing:

> "Oh, a-roaming in the gloaming
> On the bonny banks of Clyde,
> Oh, a roaming in the gloaming
> With my Bonnie by my side,
> When the sun has gone to rest
> That's the time that I love best,
> Oh it's lovely roaming in the gloaming."

What a thrill! What a miracle! We'd read about Thomas Edison's marvellous invention but now we were hearing it for the first time. Dad taught me how to run it because Mrs. Beatty just couldn't handle the machine herself, her hands shaking as they did. So whenever I'd go up there to do her errands I'd play one of the ten cylinders that had come in the box. Sure made me feel proud to operate it when many townspeople came to hear real music coming out of that big horn.

A lot of boys came too and their favorite was the cylinder called "A Man and His Dog." To hear a real dog barking out of that machine was entrancing. To all her visitors Mrs. Beatty would say over and over again, "My Jargie-Boy sent that to me. He'll be coming home to see his mother some day." About once a month to my mother she'd dictate a letter to him, her eyesight being so poor and her hands so crippled. She never got a letter until one day just before Christmas she received one saying that he had taken a week's vacation and would be arriving to spend the holiday with her. When my mother read it to Mrs. Beatty she said the old lady was so joyful she couldn't stop crying and didn't even take a sip of her tea.

When her son did arrive, Mrs. Beatty was so happy her eyes were wet all day. She'd cooked up a storm, making all his favorite foods, even saffron buns (with currant jam to go with them) and a Yorkshire pudding. At dinner she even tried to feed him a spoonful of it.

A short day for his mother, it was a very long one for the son. When he tried to describe California or talked about his jobs and experiences she would interrupt with some memory of his childhood. She talked and wept constantly. Somehow the hours went by, but after supper George had to escape so, despite her entreaties, he walked down the hill to Higley's saloon and had a couple of beers. When he returned, she wept again so he went to bed. She insisted on tucking him in.

About midnight Mrs. Beatty, as she had done many times when he was a child, took a kerosene lamp and went to the bedroom to make sure her Jargie-boy was all right. Unfortunately, her hand shook so much, the hot lamp chimney fell off on his sleeping face.

The next morning, George Beatty took the train for California. He never came back again.

****

III. *Antoine*

Big families were very common in the U.P. during the first decades of this century. In Tioga back then it was not unusual for a woman to bear eight or nine children. Some had many more. Andre Toulec down in the valley sired twenty-three but of course he had two wives, one after another I must say. No, I don't think it was the clean U.P. air or water that accounted for the fertility. Perhaps it was the weather. Most of my father's baby cases came during the months from September through December, which meant that the babies were conceived during the dog days of winter when a man couldn't go hunting or fishing. Short days and long nights! If, as someone has remarked, sex is the poetry of the poor, then there were sure a lot of poets in our little forest village.

But there were economic as well as recreational reasons for having a lot of children. Everyone of them, sons and daughters alike, had to earn their keep. The boys at the age of four were keeping the woodbox full and emptying the ashes and gathering the eggs; at seven they were

79

chopping that wood; at ten they were out trimming the limbs off the spruce their fathers were cutting for pulp. Potatoes had to be hoed; hay had to be raked; the cow and horse barns had to be cleaned. I've just hinted at the chores that were our daily lot. There were no child labor laws in Tioga.

The girls also labored mightily, sewing, washing, cooking, milking, churning butter or taking care of the younger ones. In berry time, boys and girls alike carried large pails that had to be filled before they could come home. When potato digging time arrived, children were invaluable. What I'm trying to say is that people had a lot of children because of the help they provided.

But there was another reason too. It was the fear of old age, the fear that they might have to end their days in the County Poorhouse. It was a real fear back then. There was no Social Security. There were no nursing homes for the aged. Few of our people were ever able to store away any savings except for a few bills or coins in the sugar bowl above the stove. They lived, surviving from day to day and just hoping they'd be able to make it through the next winter. Because of their hard labor most were very old at sixty, and when they hit fifty they began to worry about what would happen to them when they could work no more. Couples with many children worried the least. Surely one of their kids would take them in or stay with them. Ugly daughters were especially prized for this reason. If they didn't get married, they would have to stay home to care for the old folks.

I began to understand that fear when once my father, who served on the Health Committee of the Marquette County Board of Supervisors, took me with him as he inspected the Morgan Heights Tuberculosis Sanitorium and the County Poorhouse. The latter was an old red brick building with two wings, one for women and the other for men. It sat on the outskirts of the little city surrounded by carefully tended lawns, an apple orchard and vegetable gardens. It really looked pretty good from the outside. When we climbed the wide steps to the porch that ran alongside the front of the building, two men were sitting in chairs far apart from each other smoking pipes, but when Dad spoke to them, neither answered.

Entering the wide doorway we came into a large room with many rocking chairs along the wall, a few card tables, some bookshelves, cuspidors, and two big potbellied stoves. It was very clean but very bare. Five or six old men and three old women sat in those chairs, not speaking to each other, just rocking aimlessly. They too didn't respond to Dad's greetings. Beyond this big room was a dining hall with two long tables, and beyond that a spotless kitchen in which two cooks were busy preparing a meal. Next Dad inspected the dormitory sleeping rooms in the wings. In the women's ward all the beds were neatly made up, but in one of them was a very old lady, Mrs. Toussaint from Tioga. When she saw my father she began to cry. "Oh, Doctor," she said. "Get me out of here. Please! Please!" Dad did what he could to comfort her but made no promises. In the men's dormitory, four men, fully clothed, were lying on their cots. Dad went to each of them asking if they had any complaints. None of them answered; just stared at him with vacant eyes.

Going into the office of the superintendent of the Poorhouse, Dad complimented him on the cleanliness of the building but begged him to find some way of enriching the lives of those poor old people. "Can't be done, Doctor," the man replied. "We've tried but they're just waiting to die. You've seen the worst of them, those who've given up. The better ones are outside working in the gardens and orchard or cowbarns." When we left, I could tell that Dad was depressed. "Be sure to save your money, Cully, so you won't have to end up in a place like this," was all he said to me.

Antoine Saintonge wasn't thinking of the Poorhouse on that twentieth of June when he had his seventieth birthday. A bon jour, it was. A perfect U.P. day, warm sun, blue skies and a few lazy clouds drifting by. As he took a pail of oats down the lane to Pitou, his horse, he felt very wealthy. He had a good farm there on the old flood plain of the Tioga River, eighty acres all told. The rich soil, clay loam on top and gravel underneath, produced all the hay and oats and pasture his cow and horse required. A little stream coming from the granite hills ran inside and along the northern fence. Antoine had divided the tract into four ten-acre fields so he could rotate them every two years, one for pasture, one for clover, one for oats, one for timothy hay. Each had its own tightly strung barbed wire fence but only the pasture had a swinging gate. Antoine had never been able to save up enough money to buy the other three gates so he just moved it every two years to the field that would be the pasture.

Pitou, his horse, was drinking from the stream but when Antoine called he galloped over to get the oats. Antoine sure loved that horse. Twelve years old, it was in its prime. A good worker, very strong, Pitou could plow all day and still have enough left to pull a buggy smartly to Tioga, two miles away, then home again.

As Pitou munched the oats in the pail Antoine looked over the other three fields. The timothy stood tall and thick. No bare spots. Oui, he'd done a good job of sowing. In a few days he and Pitou would have to cut it with the mowing machine. The oats too were fine, almost heading out. Antoine loved the way the wind blew waves of bluish green across that field. After the haying was done, he and Pitou would cut that field. Antoine had already arranged with Toussaint Bergeron to have him thresh the oats in exchange for five cords of maple from the woodlot beyond the creek. Had to deliver it, of course, but with Pitou to haul the lumber wagon, that was no problem. And the clover! Never had Antoine seen a better crop. Every plant was so full of the first pink blossoms the field looked like a flower garden. Cutting that would come last but there would be more than enough for his cow all next winter. Oui, he'd even have clover hay and oats to sell for biting money. Yes, Pitou and he would make it through another winter. Antoine stroked the horse's mane. So long as he had Pitou, all was well.

When the horse had finished it went to the creek to have a drink and Antoine limped back to the house. That knee of his had been hurting badly lately. A good thing he had Pitou or he'd never be able to make it to town or, for that matter, even to take care of his big garden. It was looking good too. Widely spaced rows of potatoes, turnips, and beans would have to be cultivated soon but with the horse that was easy. Perhaps he'd have extra potatoes to sell next fall.

"Oh, mais non!" Antoine said aloud to himself. He'd forgotten to bring back the oat pail from the pasture, so he retraced his steps to get it. He'd noticed that lately he'd been becoming more forgetful. Sometimes he even fed the chickens twice. Sometimes he even forgot whether he himself had eaten. Well, what would you expect of a man seventy years old!

Hurting hard by the time he reached the house, he sat a spell on its back porch thinking about old age. Except for the bum knee he was physically in good shape. Not as strong as when he was a young buck, par certainement, but strong enough for what he had to do. He could see and hear well and had almost all his teeth. Yes, he was lonely now that his wife had died but at least he had Pitou, the horse. Too bad he and his wife had not been able to have children for his old age. It had been a great sorrow between them. No kinfolk either that he knew of. Yes, he was alone but so long as he had Pitou and the farm he didn't have to worry about going to the Poorhouse.

For a moment the old man thought about doing a washing. A good day to hang out clothes. With that breeze and sunshine they would dry in a hurry. Again he missed Maxine. She had been a good woman, good company too. That big pile of winter underwear and towels and shirts would have been long gone had she still been around. He missed her cooking and baking too. Somehow he'd never been able to bake bread like hers with the brown crust. Never! No, he'd do no washing today. Perhaps tomorrow or sometime.

Suddenly feeling very hungry, Antoine entered the kitchen. Had he eaten breakfast? The coffee pot, still warm on the range, was almost full. The dishpan full of unwashed dishes held a coffee cup on top that had a bit of coffee still in it. Oh well, it didn't matter; he was hungry, so Antoine got a cup of coffee and some korpua and took them with him out to the back steps and the June sunshine. Then he lit his old corncob pipe. All was well, tres bien!

But it wasn't! The next morning when Antoine took the pail of oats out to the pasture Pitou wasn't there! He'd forgotten to close the gate yesterday. Where was the horse? Antoine found Pitou by the creek at the far corner of the clover field. Dead! Bloated, the horse lay on its side with its belly horribly distended and with foam around its mouth. Gorging on the fresh clover had killed Pitou.

Two years later when my father made his annual inspection of the County Poorhouse he saw a man sitting in a rocker on the far side of the long porch facing the blank brick wall. It was Antoine Saintonge. Dad went over to him. "Hello, Antoine," he said. "How are things going?" Antoine didn't answer.

LAUGHING OUR WAY THROUGH WINTER

In the early years of this century from November until May the board sidewalk that lined one side of Tioga's steep hill street was completely deserted. Too much snow! We walked in the roadway when we wanted to get to the stores, school, churches or to the depot or saloon because the road was usually plowed two sleigh widths wide so one team could pass another. When the winter storms roaring down from Lake Superior deposited

four feet of the white stuff it was all we could do to keep paths shoveled out to that road or to the barn and outhouse. These paths were always kept open because we had to make it through the winter by visiting each other to share a cup of coffee or a laugh.

All of us knew the dangers of cabin fever when the snows grew as deep as the depression that threatened to overwhelm us. With no radio or TV and only a few newspapers in town, with the two-rut wagon roads closed from one village to another, with spring a thousand days away, we coped by laughing at each other's jokes and stories. In this tale I'm going to try to recall some of them.

I do so with some uneasiness because I know that you may have heard some of them before and a twice-told joke is often as flat as a cold pancake. On the other hand, since I heard them more than seventy years ago, perhaps they may still have some freshness. Here's one that started in Higley's saloon and climbed our hill from house to house in 1913:

Matti Makela, a farmer by Clowry, bought a bull, the biggest bull in the U.P. A whopper! So many people came to see it Matti thought he'd charge admission so he put up a sign in front of his house saying:

For Looking da Bull 10¢

Not many people came after news of the sign went around, but one day Erkki Salo brought his wife and thirteen kids. When he saw the sign Erkki protested. "Too much raha," he said. "I no pay dollar fifty for see your bull, no! You give discount, mebbe, eh?" Matti counted the children. "All dose kids yours, Erkki?" he asked. "Yah, dey mine." "Well," said Matti, "I pay you dollar fifty for having mine bull look at you."

Many of those stories were told using a heavy foreign accent, because most of our people were immigrants from the old countries overseas and their speech reflected their origins. Consequently, since the jokes lose some of their flavor when put on a printed page, I shall just hint at their dialects. Here's one involving the Swedish foreign accent that uses *y* for the *j* sound as in "My name is Yonny Yohnson and I come from Visconsin."

Eino Ysitalo came home early one afternoon from cutting pulp to find his wife, Lena, coming out of the barn with her face flushed and with hay in her hair. "I been cleaning barn for you, Eino" she explained. But Eino had noticed that a man's footprints in the snow had led to the barn along with hers. "Mebbe so, mebbe so, but I tink mebbe you been having some nooky wit dat Swede fellow been hanging round. You come wit me!"

Going to the barn, Eino looked all over but didn't find anything except that there was a big pile of stuff in the corner. "What dis?" he asked.

"Oh dat just pile junk for haul away in spring. I told you I clean barn. Just old boards, harness, horse blankets, jingle bells for sleigh. Old stuff, no good."

Eino gave the heap a good kick. "Yingle, yingle," said the pile.

Because Tioga was a melting pot of many nationalities there were hundreds of jokes in which they poked fun at each other. Often the same joke about the dumb Swede would be told about the dumb Norwegian if a person of Swédish descent were telling it. For example:

Leif Backe and Alf Preus, two old Norwegian lumberjacks decided to go ice fishing, though neither of them had ever done so nor knew anything about it. They fished for two hours and never had a bite, although they noticed that a man further out on the ice kept catching one fish after another. So when the man left they decided to go where he had been and fish there. When they did, Leif said, "Hey Alf, Look! He make hole in ice."

Some of the things that were passed from house to house were not jokes at all. They were "sayings." "Two can live as cheaply as one if they are a flea and his dog." "Every minnow wants to be a pike." "Never look down the outhouse hole." "The only thing stinks worse than a dead horse is a Frenchman in the sauna."

One of those sayings always puzzled me as a kid. It was "Lots of water in the swamp for you" and was used as a statement of rejection, as the equivalent of "No!" Then one day an old Finn told me its origin. An Irishman on one of the few hot days of a U.P. summer had gone up to the door of Mrs. Koski's farmhouse and asked for a drink of water. "What national are you?" "I'm Irish," he said. "There's lotsa water in the swamp for you, you Catolic!" she yelled and slammed the door.

In those early days there was much enmity between nationalities, partly because of religion and partly because of old prejudices brought to Tioga from the old country. The Protestants hated the Catholics; the Swedes the Norwegians, the French the Finns, and so on. Now they're all intermarried and the old antagonisms are gone, but back then they were hot indeed. One example:

A Swede lumberjack named Sven Anderson came out of the woods at breakup time for his annual spree, spent a lot of his money setting up drinks at Higley's saloon and was so drunk when he arrived at our whorehouse they wouldn't let him in. Sven staggered around outside for a bit in the cold, then crawled in Alphonse Verlaine's pig house to sleep it off. Finally next morning, when he began to come to he felt a warm body beside him. Still with his eyes shut, he put his arms around the warm body and murmured affectionately, "Ar du Svensk?" (Are you Swedish?) "Norsk, Norsk," said the pig and Sven tore out of the pigpen yelling "I vant mine money back!" (Norsk means Norwegian).

And there was the tale about old man Joe LaCosse who ran a tavern up at Big Bay. It seems that a Finn riverman had been killed in a log jam on the Yellow Dog River, and some of his friends were soliciting funds to give him a decent funeral. Although they knew that Joe hated Finns, they asked him for a dollar to help do it. "Zat man who die, he Frenchman, oui?" Joe asked. "No, he's Finn," they replied. Joe pulls out his wallet and gives them four dollars. "Bury four of dem," he said.

Lon Boland, a young Cornish miner, married Jenny but she was lazy as well as pretty. Didn't know how to bake a pasty or pudding or saffron bread. Didn't clean the house well. Didn't fill his dinner pail even though he worked the night shift at the mine. Lon stood it for a long time, but one morning coming home from work he noticed that there was smoke coming out of the chimney of every house in Tioga but his. As he had expected, his lazy wife was still sleeping and the house was cold. So Lon lowered a twelve-quart pail into the well, pulled it up, then threw it onto Jenny's face, yelling "Fire! Fire! Fire!" Jenny jumps out of bed. "Where? Where the fire?" "In every bloody house in town but ours!"

Another Cousin Jack story: When telephones first came to Tioga they could be found in only four places; in the mining office, in the company store, in the doctor's house and in the mining captain's home. Though many of our people were curious, and some believed that it was impossible to talk through wires, most of them feared using them. Next to the mining captain's house lived a hard-rock Cornish miner named Johnny Lowe who worked nights but slept days. One day his wife, Thirsa, a big powerful woman who regularly beat up her husband, hung up the clothes to dry then went to Ishpeming to see her daughter, but when it started to rain and thunder she said she had to take the train back home. "Your feyther will never ha' the sense to bring in the wash," she said. Her daughter had a better idea. "Mither, why don't 'ee use my new telyphone and call up Cap'n Campton and ask him to go over and get feyther to talk to you and then you can tell him what to do?" So they did and Cap'n Campton goes over to Johnny Rowe's house and said, "Johnny, your missus wants to talk to ye on my telyphone so come over and I'll show ye what to do." The phone, of course, was one of the old fashioned box kind hung on the wall. "Now Johnny," said the Captain, "You stand up against that h'instrument, put yer mouth against that pipe and hold that horn agin yer ear. Then say 'Ello' and the missus will be talking to 'ee." Johnny did as he was told but just as he said 'ello' a bolt of lightning hit the line and knocked him down. Picking himself up, he looked at the Captain and said, "Aye, that's my bloody old lady, for sure."

Another, still another: A Cousin Jack miner came to work one morning and told his partner on the drilling crew, "Well, Jimmy, great thing come to my house last night." "And what was that?" "We 'ad driblets come, we did." "Driblets? What's driblets, never hear of driblets?" asked Jimmy. His friend told him his wife had just given birth to three babies all at once. "Can't believe it," said Jimmy, "Taint possible." "We finish this shift and you come to my 'ouse and I show 'ee." So they did and when Jimmy saw the three fine babies, he exclaimed, "Ah, but they be grand indeed. Never seen nawthing like it in my life." Then, pointing to the middle one, he said "Damn, pardner, if it were me, I'd keep this one."

The Finns had quite a sense of humor too. Arne Sippola amused himself and others of us by painting signs and then placing them way back in the woods. Half way to Republic in the middle of a cedar swamp I once saw one of those signs saying, "You are Here!"

Seppo Keski was an old Finlander who spent all his free time fishing for pike on Lake Tioga, at least all of it that wasn't spent down at Higley's saloon singing lugubrious Finnish songs when he got lubricated right. He never went to church and only once a year to the sauna but he had a gay spirit. Yes, everyone liked that dissolute old character, at least everyone except the Finnish pastor who thoroughly disapproved of the old scoundrel. Meeting Seppo on the street one day, the pastor gave him the devil for his evil ways. "You going to hell, Seppo. You getting old, not much more time for being saved." And then the preacher painted a word picture of Seppo's destination, the devils with pitchforks, the glowing coals, the lake of fire. Seppo interrupted. "You say hell got lake of fire?" "Yah," said the preacher. "Good," said Seppo. "Den I fish forever and when I catch fish dey already cooked."

We also enjoyed what we called happenings, true stories of incidents that had occurred in Tioga. Here's one: "We had a flock of laying chickens on our farm by Half Way and one summer some varmint began killing one or two every night. Well, my father got fed up with that and staked out one of his hunting dogs to a tree beside the chicken coop, knowing that the dog would start yelping when the varmint come around. Now as I said, this was summer so Dad was wearing a short nightshirt to bed instead of the long underwear he used in winter time. Well, he loaded up his double-barreled shotgun and was sleeping when he heard the dog howling, so he gets up and sneaks out to the chicken coop but untied the hound first so if he couldn't see to shoot, it being so dark, the dog might get the critter. Once he opened the door, Dad first couldn't see anything it being so black in there, but then he saw something moving on the floor, raised up to aim and just then that old hound dog, he poked his cold nose under my father's nightshirt. Pow! When the feathers settled we had seven chickens to clean but never saw that varmint at all." That story had Tioga laughing for a week even though it snowed every day.

THE OLD LOGGING DAYS

I was born too late, in 1905, to have known the great white pine forest that covered the Upper Peninsula of Michigan. The last log drive down one of Tioga River's tributaries, Wabeek Creek, occurred when I was seven years old, but throughout my childhood I was entranced by the tales of the old lumberjacks who had logged off that great forest. Actually they weren't very old, perhaps in their late forties or fifties, young enough to recall fondly the heroic or dirty deeds of their own rambunctious youth. Pete Ramos was one of them. Physically broken by terribly hard labor in the woods and by alcohol, it wasn't hard to get him started if he were only half drunk, and I'd brought him one of my father's cigars.

"Tell me how they logged off the Tioga in the old days?" I'd beg. "What happened first?"

"First?" Pete looked puzzled. "Well, I guess Silverthorne and Company bought them a big chunk of land, maybe seventy, eighty sections on both sides of the river. That's over three hundred forties. Got it from the government for about a dollar an acre, they did. Damned steal, it was. And after they logged the lower part of the river they bought a lot more upstream. That was when I started working for 'em up at Camp 10 by the Haysheds dam. I helped build that dam and was lucky. Two men got killed doing it."

Pete told me that the big logging company hired timber cruisers (landlookers) to explore the area first, estimating the amound of board feet of prime pine in each forty acres, locating the camp site and figuring out where the logging dams should be built so that a sufficient head of water could be stored to float the logs down the river to Lake Tioga where the sawmill was.

"Them cruisers had to be damned good," Pete said. "Had to find the corner posts of the sections so they'd know where one forty left off and another begin. Had to lay out where the roads would run level enough for icing. Had to size up a big pine and say it'd make maybe nine sawlogs and go maybe 8,000 board feet. I was thinking to be a cruiser myself but I went in the bush with one once and knows I never had the brains for it. Naw, just a lumberjack and riverman, that was all I could be and all I ever wuz."

"You mentioned that you helped build the Haysheds dam. Did you do that before the lumber camps were built?" I asked.

"Yes and no," Pete replied. "I was on a crew of maybe thirty men, but we had to repair the other dams lower on the river while the camps were built: Rock Dam, Plank Dam, and Brown's Dam, oh yeah, and the Wabeek Dam too. Lived in tents and the bugs were awful. When we got done with that job and started on the Haysheds they had the bunkhouse roof on but no windows or bunks, so we slept on the floor."

"I've been up to that dam with my father," I said. "It sure was a good place to put it."

"Yeah, the only notch in them big granite hills. When it was full there was a lake two mile long behind it. Had a big waterfall there before we cribbed it."

"What's cribbing?" I inquired.

"You don't know what cribbing is?" Pete was incredulous. "It's big boxes made of big logs spiked together on the corners. Some of them spikes were two feet long or more. Made you grunt sledging them. Then we filled 'em with rocks and dirt and put one crib on top another till they was high enough."

"But what did you do with the water, the river I mean?"

"Dammed off one side at a time. Trick come when we had to join the cribs in the middle. That's when Pat Leahy got kilt. Had a big log beam fall on him when he wuz putting up the underpinning for the sluice gate. Never knowed what happened to him, it come so sudden."

"Did they bring him to town to bury him?"

"Hell no," said Pete. "Just dug a hole and put 'im in it back in the bush with rocks on top to keep out the wolves. We did nail one of his boots to a tree along the river. One time I counted eight boots like that along the bank trail. Lot of men got killed in the woods back then, but me, I got my boots on even now." Dad's cigar had been finished and the old man left for Higley's saloon. I was a bit shaken remembering that once I'd seen the remnants of such an old boot on the bank of the river.

I was also sorry he had left before I could learn more about the lumber camps and the lumberjacks, but I soon had an even better informant. It happened like this. One afternoon I rode my old white horse, Billy, down the big hill behind Delongchamp's farm to the west branch of the Escanaba to do some wet fly fishing for trout. They bit very slowly and I suddenly realized it was getting late so I headed back, meeting my father in his 1914 Ford coming to find me. "It's suppertime," he said crossly, "your mother is worried. She said you told her you'd be back by five. So get going!"

While he turned his car around on the Furnace road, I got Billy into a good gallop and foolishly galloped him across the railroad tracks by the depot. Catching his horseshoe in the crossing boards he fell heavily upon me, breaking my right leg in two places, above and below the knee. Well, Dad was right there so he took me home and soon had me in a heavy plaster cast from hip to toe. The next month I spent up in Grandma Van's room regretting my folly. However, some good came out of the accident. Dad hired Anders Lundberg, an old Swede carpenter, to put new sashes in the windows of that room so they could be opened easily, and I soon discovered that Anders had been the boss carpenter when they built Camp 10 at the Haysheds. Moreover, once the windows had been fixed, Dad hired him to teach me to play the guitar, probably because he couldn't bear hearing me pick out tunes on a primitive instrument I'd made out of a cigar box and strung with one of the catgut sutures he used for sewing up wounds. So I had a fine opportunity to learn a lot about the old logging days from Anders too.

"We started building the camps in May month," the old man said, "and had them all done by October. A helluva big job it was. We turned that beaver meadow into a small town. They hired four log butchers to help me and a crew of about twenty jacks, and two team of horses. The big boss, Mike Terson, told me to build his cabin first, then the cook and bunk shacks, then the ox and horse barn with a blacksmith shop joined to the barn. He said the cabin for the clerk and scaler could come later. There would be a crew of a hundred men working there for two or three years. I still don't know how we got it done in time for the fall cutting."

"How big were the buildings?" I asked.

"Lemme see. The bunkhouse was 80 by 40 feet. That was the biggest one. Had to be because on each side we built 25 double bunks to hold four men each, with deacon seats running in front of them."

91

"What's a deacon seat, Anders?"

"That's a long bench where the men sat. No chairs in camp. On Sundays when the jacks played cards or filed their saws and axes they sat on nail kegs."

"I suppose they heated it with those long stoves I've seen pictures of," I said.

"Yah," he replied. "Long square ones, two of them, that could take five-foot logs and burn all night. Above them they had wood racks and haywire to hang their clothes for drying, and beside them the hot water barrel fed by copper pipe from a coil of it inside the stove. It was so warm in there even when it was twenty below what with the body heat and all that later we had to put two skylights into the roof that could be opened to let out the stink. Only four windows, so it was dark in there even in daylight, and the coal oil lanterns were always burning until lights out at 9 o'clock."

"Did the men eat in the bunkhouse?" I asked.

"Oh no," said Anders. "We built another shack for eating but I misremember exactly how big. Must have been over fifty feet long and thirty feet across because the two tables in them were forty feet long. Even then the men had to eat in two shifts, half an hour apart. Camp 10 had two cookees, young kids who hauled in the food and cleared the tables for the next batch of eaters. They also tended the fires and swept and did all the dirty jobs around the kitchen and cook shack. Tough job in camp being a cookee."

"Anders, I've heard that nobody was supposed to talk at mealtime. Is that right?"

"You damned tooting!" he replied. "Oh you could ask for someone to pass the potatoes or stew but nothing else. No conversation. If there was, the bull cook would come in with his cleaver. No, we ate silent. Every logging camp had that rule."

"Feeding a hundred men must have been a real job," I said. "How many cookstoves did they have?"

"Three big kitchen ranges at Camp 10," Anders answered. "They were in the cook shack, a different building but joined to the dining shack by a door. The cook and chore boys slept there at one end, not in the bunkhouse, having to get up at two, three in the morning to start breakfast."

"I hear they fed them good," I said.

"Yah, Silverthorne's camps anyway did. Breakfast at six o'clock still dark had pancakes and molasses, sowbelly, oatmeal, bread and coffee, all you could eat. They brung it in big dishpans for the table. Supper the biggest meal. Big pots of stew, venison or beef or pork. Always potatoes, beans (we called 'em firecrackers) and fresh bread. Pies too. Some camps didn't have it so good but Silverthorne's always. That's how they kept the best jacks."

"What about lunch?" I asked. "Did they come back for that?"

92

"Naw! Teamsters hauled dishpans full of sandwiches, ham often, out to the cuttings, along with ten gallon kettles of hot tea wrapped in blankets to keep them warm. Can of sugar lumps too. Men had only half an hour to eat it, then back to work until too dark to see. Long hours, them."

"Tell me about the horse barns," I begged.

Anders thought for a moment. "They had two of them up at Camp 10, fifty feet long and thirty wide. Ox stalls on north end and horse stalls along sides. No stoves. Didn't need 'em. Next to it we built the blacksmith shop, thirty by twenty feet. Had two forges and the blacksmith slept there. Blacksmith always important man in lumbercamp. Made sleds, jammmers, runners, chains, wagon wheels, hinges, anything, and shoed horses of course. I helped on sleds and wheels."

"What's a jammer?" I inquired.

"An outfit, like a derrick, for lifting logs. Them big pine logs sure were heavy. Most of the time though, the loaders could put twenty, thirty, sixteen-foot logs on the sleighs just using canthooks and rolling them up on stringers before chaining them tight. I hear tell that up at Ontonagon in the late 1800s they hauled fifty logs on one sleigh. Took a ton of half-inch chain to hold them and only two horses pulled that load. Of course the roads were iced with ruts carved in them so the sleighs wouldn't slip sidewise."

"You said something about having to build a clerk and scaler's shack. What did they do and why did they have their own buildings?"

Anders lit his pipe. "Most camps had just one man for both jobs but Camp 10 had two. The scaler, he measured butts of all logs when they was on the sleighs and make estimate of how many board feet for each one. Put it down in notebook and put blue chalk mark to show he'd done it. Sometimes he'd use sledge with Silverthorne marker *ST* so when logs get to sawmill they know whose it was. They did that when different companies were logging same rivershed. The clerk, he was company man. He keep accounts of how much wood was cut and also he keep store. The jacks could buy blankets, tobacco, files, axes, shirts, things like that in the store and charge them against their wages."

"Did they pay them off only in the spring?" I asked.

"Yah, but he just give piece of paper showing how much, maybe four, five hundred dollars, but then the jack had to walk maybe twenty miles to Tioga or to headquarters camp to get cash; often in gold."

"And then they blew it," I said.

"Not all of them. Some family men, they didn't but most hit for the saloons right away. Had to have big spree after being up there in the bush so long."

I'd hoped that Anders could tell me more about the actual cutting and hauling, but he really didn't know much about it. He wanted to tell me about how the lumber camps were built.

"When we first got to the beaver meadow there was a thick stand of white pine, all 150 feet tall, just beyond the creek, and we used them for the logs. Used the biggest ones for the foundation. Put on the next log with the butt on the other end and so on. Had to square off the top and bottom of each of 'em so they'd fit tight when notched at the ends. Used a broadaxe for that."

"What's a broadaxe?" I asked.

"A big axe with a blade three times as big as ordinary one. Would weigh maybe sixteen pounds. One of the log butchers on my crew, Axel Aronson, his name was, could slab a log better than anyone, better than I could, leaving the surface of that log so smooth it looked like it had been planed. And never went beyond the blue line either."

What's the blue line, Anders?"

"Got to have one to keep the cut straight," he said. "To mark and score you chalk a line good with blue chalk, put one end of it on the butt of a log, then stretch it tight all along the length, fastening it tight on the other end. Then you hold about three feet of the line out from one end, pull it up, and then snap it down hard. That'll leave a straight blue mark on the log. Then you move on and do it again and again. I'll show you how on the guitar." He illustrated.

There was much more that I've forgotten, but it was certain that old Anders knew his stuff about building if not logging. The latter information came to me from other old men whom I quizzed later after I could walk again.

In the early days, they told me, they had to fell the trees with double-bitted axes, but soon crosscut saws appeared and they were of course much more efficient. The cutters first made a deep horizontal cut across the base of the tree about waist-high, chopped out a triangular notch, then went to the other side of the tree and made another horizontal saw cut above it until the tree cracked, groaned and toppled. A good sawyer could drive a stake and then put that great pine right on top of it, driving it into the ground. Some real skill was involved in figuring out the effects of wind and the lay of the land, as well as in the sawing itself. One old man told me how he'd knocked the man on the opposite end of the saw on his ass when he hadn't done his fair share of the pulling and pushing. "If you gonna ride the saw den you might as well sit down," he said. It was very hard labor. A good lumberjack, and they prided themselves on being one, could cut, with his partner, perhaps four or five of those tall pines in a single day, one that lasted from daybreak to dark. Having seen stumps of those pines that measured seven feet across, I cannot understand how they could have done so much in a single day but they rarely rested. They couldn't even smoke their pipes because that would take too much time. Instead they chewed tobacco. "Every stump, it had a ring of brown tobacco juice around it," one man told me.

The lumberjacks who did the cutting were top dogs in the hierarchy, kings of the woods. Below them came the buckers, the men who sawed up the fallen logs into sixteen-foot lengths, trimming off the branches. Below these were the swampers and skidders who, with oxen or horses, "snaked" those logs to the nearest logging trail, a road that was made as level as possible, and then iced so the big lumber sleighs or sleds could haul them to the rollways or landings at the edge of the river. There they were stacked in huge piles to await the spring thaws and the torrents of water released from the logging dams that would float them down the Tioga River to the sawmills at Lake Tioga.

Teamsters were also among the elite, especially those who could handle the oxen. When the land was fairly level, horses could be used to "twitch" or skid the big logs down to the iced river road, but when they were down in a gully or up on a hill the oxen did a better job. Huge, castrated bulls of various breeds, and well-trained, they could snake out those big logs with their powerful steady pulling. Ox teamsters used no reins; they had twitches, long whips with which they touched the oxen's heads to steer them right or left on the skidding paths or to urge them to pull harder, with accompanying yells of "Gee" (for right) or "Haw!" (for left). Many of the best teamsters were French Canadians.

All of the old men agreed that the worst job in camp was that of "bucket monkey". Since the river roads had to be kept paved with ice and the work was done at night when water froze best, the bucket monkey had to fill the large square tank of the sprinkler sleigh from the nearest pond or stream. Sometimes they filled it by hand, sometimes using a jammer with a bucket. Always wet and half frozen, the men had to fill those tanks over and over again each night, so that the heavy log sleighs could glide easily over the iced pavement down to the banking area. Ruts were also made in the ice so the sleighs wouldn't slip sideways.

One of the most dangerous jobs involved the loading, unloading, and stacking of the logs, especially at the rollways by the river. There the logs were piled horizontally along a slanting bank so that in the spring break-up they could be rolled down into the stream after the bottom key log was loosened. Since some of those logs weighed almost a ton, many accidents occurred at the rollways. One old lumberjack told me a harrowing tale about one such mishap.

"Me, I tell ze woods boss, ze stack beeg enough," he said. "No more log or she let go, but he say put more on. Me an' Raoul we on top of her to make straight with canthook. Den Ow! She go like tonnaire (thunder). Me, I jump off side but Raoul he go weeth logs down ze bank. We no find anysing of Raoul, my fren'. Dey grind him to nuttin! Oui, dey make pea soup of him."

When the spring breakup came, most of the lumberjacks were discharged except for those who would participate in the drives, in floating the logs down river to Lake Tioga and its sawmills. After being in the woods for six or seven months, and with plenty of money in their pockets, it was time for the annual spree. How those old men liked to tell about it!

"We hadn't had a drink or seen a woman all winter," they told me. "We couldn't fight in camp but we sure made up for it when breakup come." Tioga's ten-bed whore house was busy day and night because they'd added six or seven more girls who came up on the train from Milwaukee. Higley's saloon was jumping too. But most of the jacks took the train for Ishpeming or Seney where service was better. Oh the fighting that went on! My father, the doctor, sewed on ears and noses that had been bitten off, and dressed the gouges and bruises if they were bad enough. Men fought until one went down and then the other stomped on his face, twisting the caulks of his boots so that he would always be remembered. They fought without reason as brutally as possible. "I kin lick any man in the house," one would yell, and there were always takers of his challenge. It was the code!

"Gad, we wuz horny when we come out the woods," one old bugger said. "Had to find a woman right away. I seen one jack at Seney kick in the window of a store with his boots to get at a whatyoucallit, statue like of a woman (manikin), and he screwed that statue up and down the street."

The lumberjacks though had a great respect for decent women and would take off their hats to them when meeting one on the street. Most of the hell-raising in Tioga took place downtown in the valley by the saloon and depot so they rarely came up the long hill street for their brawling. The few who did were so drunk they didn't know any better and Charley Olafson, our constable, put them to bed in the cages of our jail in the town hall until they sobered up. Higley's saloon, like most of those in the U.P. also had a holding tank, a back room where lumberjacks were stacked until they sobered up. No big deal!

Back at Silverthorne's camp, the men chosen to drive the logs downriver filed the corks (caulks) of their boots and sharpened their pike-poles. These rivermen were a select crew, agile and fearless, the best of the lot. They had to be! Breaking the huge stacks of logs on the rollways so they would cascade into the river or into the ponds above the logging dam, they had to shepherd those logs all the way downstream. This often called for running across the slippery logs floating crazily in the torrent of water released from the dam. They had to prevent them from crisscrossing and forming the dreaded log jams, those massive tangles of logs that could back up the water for miles. The river hogs, as they called themselves, were stationed at half-mile intervals along the stream and when one of them saw that a log jam might be forming he'd let out the alarm cry "Ah-eeee!". This would be echoed by the men above and below him, and soon enough rivermen would be assembled at the spot so they could try to pry or dynamite out the key log that held the jam tight. Once the logs started moving again, the men had to make their way precariously to shore, leaping from log to log. One misstep meant death. There were many casualties on those river drives, many boots to be nailed to the trees along the riverbank.

To keep the logs moving, one dam after another was opened in turn, first the Hayshed dam, then the Brown's dam, then the Plank dam. The rivermen slept in the snow beside the stream but were fed from the wanigan, a barge-like raft that carried the cookshack and tool shed. It was a rough life, a dangerous one!

Somehow they got the logs to Lake Tioga. There they were assembled into large rafts enclosed by boom logs and blown by the prevailing west wind to the sawmill at the east end of the lake. When the wind didn't blow hard enough and the rafts stalled, a procedure called kedging was used. At the head end of the log raft a platform was built, and on it was fastened a large vertical spool called a capstan, wound with heavy rope or cable. Then a large anchor was put in a rowboat and dropped off ahead of the raft. Its rope was then fastened to that of the capstan, and by great effort men could turn the capstan so the raft could be winched forward. They prayed for wind, those men on the double shift than manned the spokes of the huge spool. Somehow year after year, they got the logs to the mill.

And when they did, all hell broke loose in Tioga again. The terribly long winter and the constant dangers had stored up hungers for booze and women and mayhem that few of the riverhogs could resist. Again the holding tank at Higley's saloon had them stacked up like cordwood; Charley Olafson's jail overflowed and our red whorehouse needed more beds and girls. Then suddenly it was all over. Peace returned to Tioga as though nothing had happened. Only one memento was left: a pair of lumberjack boots nailed to the whorehouse door.

TEACHING MY BRIDE TO FISH

When my new wife and I stopped off at Tioga on our way to the Old Cabin for our honeymoon, I asked my father jokingly if he had any wise advice about how I could have a happy marriage. "Yes," he said. "Just one thing: don't ever teach your wife to hunt or fish!"

That didn't make any sense to me back then, though there have been a few times in the ensuing years when I felt he was right. Of course I'd teach Milove to fish. Brook trout fishing had been the best part of my existence since I caught that first speckled beauty at the age of six and became hooked forever. To think that I could not share all the delights of that lovely addiction with the woman I loved, well, that was unthinkable!

It's almost impossible to explain the fascination of trout fishing to anyone who has not enjoyed it. Why do we love to fish for *salmon fontinalis* (trout of springs)? Certainly it is not for the poundage. The biggest one I ever caught was just a shade under three pounds and most were no longer than ten inches. Nor is it the battle they put up - though ounce for ounce, a brook trout will hold its own with any fish. I've caught bass, pike, salmon, steelhead, bonefish and salmon that put on spectacular fights that left me exhausted, but I'd rather catch an eight-inch trout in the U.P. than any of them. Nor is it their edibility, wonderful as that may be when trout are broiled or sizzled in a frying pan over a campfire just after being caught.

I believe that the reason lies in where trout are caught, how they are caught, and when. Brook trout are the children of the dawn and dusk; that is when they are most active. How often have I set the alarm, snatched a quick breakfast and then hiked up logging roads, watching the white mist over the river become pink with the first rays of the sun! Even in the old days when there were lots of trout, they usually stopped biting by nine o'clock and did not resume until the evening sun descended behind our huge hills in a burst of glorious sunset.

Perhaps I've loved brook trout fishing because they're more beautiful than any other fish, yes, even more beautiful than an arctic grayling. A freshly caught brook trout with its iridescent scarlet spots is breath-taking. I'm sure they get that way because they live out their lives in beautiful surroundings. Preferring the smaller, rocky streams, they seem to select the loveliest rapids, waterfalls, and pools as their habitat. Sometimes at night when I cannot sleep I drowsily let my mind wander up the Tioga River and its tributaries recalling where I had caught them. Invariably, every one of those spots is a beautiful one.

Much of the pleasure in trout fishing comes from the challenge it presents. It isn't easy fishing. You walk upstream a long way then slowly wade down, feeling the slippery rocks underfoot lest you use your nose for a cane. You never hurry! Splashing would disturb the trout below you and besides, you might miss seeing something on the riverbank. Constantly, you "read the stream," seeking to discover where the fish may lie. "Ah, there beside that sunken boulder should be a good place!" "There ought to be one under that white foam where that eddy comes out from under the bushes." "Will the trout be at the head of the pool in the fast water or down at the tail near that snag?" You become so completely engrossed in this constant evaluation of probabilities that all your little cares and worries disappear. The happy hours go by before you know it.

Then too, when you have located a spot where a trout might be, you must devise strategies for attracting and taking him. Often, when wading down the middle of a stream, you can cast your bait directly ahead of you, letting the current take it to the trout, and nudging the hook along the bottom. Never cast directly at the trout or he will bolt for cover. Often it's wiser to make your cast from the side of the pool or rapids, allowing the line to swing in an arc so it passes directly over the possible fish. If the rising or setting sun is directly behind you, projecting your moving shadow onto the surface, you don't have a chance! Trout are very sensitive to fleeting shadows and also to vibrations, so you also have to walk very carefully even when you are on the riverbank.

Like all U.P. trout fishermen, I began by using worms for bait and although I graduated to using flies, thanks to my Grampa Gage, I never became a purist. Unto their tastes, has been my motto. There's almost as much skill involved in bait fishing as in fly casting if you do it right. For example, there are three kinds of worms, each of which under certain circumstances, will take trout when the others won't. On a warm, windless day when the surface of the pool mirrors white clouds lazily floating across a blue sky, five or six tiny redworms on a hook allowed to settle on the bottom for ten minutes will entice a wary trout. Leaf worms, so-called because that's where you find them, are bigger and not so wiggly, but if you string two of them on a hook below a little golden spinner you'll find them excellent in a roaring rapids. When you find a pool full of little trout or trout that you don't want to catch, and they are always the first to bite, a big glob of night crawler will do the job. My father never used anything but those crawlers and he usually caught bigger fish than I did, but not as many.

There's even an art to putting worms on hooks, as I learned one evening from Laf Bodine, Tioga's best poacher, who showed me fourteen different ways of doing so. There are sunny summer days when only a grasshopper thrashing on the surface will yield a strike. I've caught bigger trout on two-inch minnows, on a belly slice from a hapless perch, on white grubs, and some little ones on yellow kernels of canned sweet corn. But enough! Although I've barely scratched the surface of my topic and could write a whole book about trout fishing, I fear I'm in danger of losing a reader or two, so let me tell how I taught my new wife to fish.

We had spent a fine morning and early afternoon walking the trails around our big lake, climbing Porcupine Bluff to see the caves among its huge boulders, having a drink from the big spring, crossing the outlet on a beaver dam, and finally circling the north shore back to the old cabin. I let Milove lead the way, not only to intercept the cobwebs across the path but because half of the fun lies in following the blazes on the trees and recognizing them. Only once did she lose the trail. Yes, she would make me a fine wife.

We were tired and hungry after the long jaunt, so after eating two cookies we lay down in the upper bunk to rest in each other's arms. After about an hour I awakened to find her gone and to hear her messing with some pans. "What will you have, Milord?" she asked. "Canned corned beef with potatoes, or potatoes with corned beef?"

"Neither," I replied. "We're having brook trout for supper and you'll have to catch them." I climbed down from the upper bunk and put the coffee pail, frying pan, two cups, two forks, a thick slice of bacon, and some salt and flour into my packsack. Leaving the cabin, I also carried a small can of leaf worms, my tackle bag, and the new bamboo flyrod I'd purchased for her wedding present. I was anxious to see how it would work. Lord knows, it should cast well. A wisp of a rod, only seven feet, three inches long and weighing only four ounces, I had paid the Orvis Company much more for it than I should have afforded.

Soon we were at the big pool on Wabeek Creek just below the old logging dam. It's a lovely spot and often I'd dreamed that someday I might take a wife or lover there. A long pool and a wide one with a torrent of silvery water cascading into it from the apron of the dam's sluice gate, it always held some trout though often they did not bite. On the southern shore, a spring entered the pool from under some bushes and flowed into submerged boulders and sunken logs over which an eddy circled strings of foam. The north bank where we stood, however, had a little grassy clearing where ovals of dead embers showed that other fishermen had built coffee fires there. Yes, it was the right place and the right time too because the sun had just begun to descend behind the hills. A lovely place!

"I'll make our cooking fire here, Milove," I said, "but you'll have to catch our supper. If you don't it will be a sparse one, just coffee, korpua, and that one strip of bacon, so assemble the rod. Be sure to join the two pieces so that the guides are in line."

Noticing that she was having difficulty, I took the two pieces of the rod from her. "Observe, woman!" I said pontifically. "This silver place where they join is called a ferrule. The upper section ends in the male part of the ferule; the lower section ends in the hollow female part. You have to marry them. Here, I'll show you."

"Yes, sire," she replied. But I was having difficulty too. Brand new rods are like that at first before they're broken in. Explaining that some grease was needed and that the sebaceous glands along the side of the nose held just the right amount. I began to twirl the end of the upper section against it. Suddenly Milove began to giggle outrageously and when I asked her how come she said, "That's the first time I ever saw a man wiping his nose with his p- pe-" She couldn't say the word but went into another burst of giggling. Then, noticing that I was still having trouble getting the male end all the way in, she took it from me and soon had them joined tightly. "Cully," she said, still giggling, "This reminds me of our wedding night."

I had her then put on the reel, string the black braided line through the guides, and then tie on the seven-foot leader which I'd had soaking at the edge of the stream. "No," I said, "That's a poor knot. Do it like this, Woman."

101

"Don't call me woman!" she exclaimed, "or I'll start calling you Man. I'm your blushing bride, remember?"

Then came the baiting of the hook I'd attached. I did it first, threading one of the leaf worms up the shank and over the knot, then looping another one around the curve and barb so the tips of both ends could wiggle freely. Stripping off the worms, I handed her the bare hook for rebaiting. "Now you do it, wo...Milove," I said. "You're a fast learner, Mr. Gage," she replied. "And so are you Madam," I responded, admiring how well she'd strung on the wigglers. "Now try a few casts from here, stripping some line off the reel with your left hand first in loops, then flicking the rod forward until it's all gone." She caught on immediately.

I told her to go over to the big log beam at the base of the dam, cast the bait into the current, and let it go downstream until it came close to a gray snag that was sticking out of the water, then wait and do it again and again until you get a bite. "You may have to pull out more line from the reel to reach the spot." I suggested.

Nothing happened on that first cast so I told her to crank the line back on the reel and begin again, and not to point the rod at the bait but to keep the tip high, and that if she had a bite, to jerk the tip back slightly so she could hook the fish. She grinned and saluted mockingly, but when a fish grabbed the bait she let out a war whoop. "I've got one, Cully," she yelled. "I've got one. Now what do I do? Do I crank the spool?"

I told her to keep a taut line and to walk over beside me where I'd hand her the little green net to lift it out of the water, and not to say spool. It was a reel, not a spool. She had some trouble holding the rod with her left hand behind her as she scooped the fish into the net. "Oh, what a beauty!" she exclaimed. "I've caught my first trout ever."

"No, you haven't" I interrupted. "That's just a damned chub, an eight-inch chub, the ugliest fish in the river. A nuisance fish, soft and inedible. I'll show you how to take it off this time but never again, so watch. Hold it firmly around its sides with one hand, then pry out the hook with the other. See?" I threw the chub up into the bushes as I've always done. "Don't! Don't," she screamed, as she ran over to find it. "Poor little fishy in the bush, let me put you back where you belong," she said as she picked it up and let it swim away. "Well, anyway, she's not squeamish," I thought, "but she sure has a lot to learn."

After putting three leaf worms instead of two on the hook, she returned to the dam and cast again into the current. I saw the line jerk slightly and heard her yelp. "Cully, I've got another bite but it's different, harder. There's another."

"Let it have it," I shouted above the roar of the water coming over the dam. "Take up the slack till you feel the fish." I saw the line moving steadily sideways. "OK, strike it! Jerk the tip of your rod." The trout was hooked and on that little rod it put up a terrific fight all over the lower pool. Once it broke water and I could see that it was a good one.

Don't give it any slack," I yelled. "Keep the rod tip high!" Once when it headed right for the snag I said a little prayer and the big trout turned away just before the leader was wrapped around it. Back and forth the trout surged, but finally its struggles diminished enough so she could lead it to the bank where I stood and slide it up onto the sand and gravel. "Oh, I forgot about netting it," Milove exclaimed shakily as I pounced upon the fish and laid it on some moss far from the water's edge.

"Oh, you beautiful, beautiful thing," she said. "Cully, let's put it back before it dies."

"Like hell," I roared. "That's our supper and I'm hungry. Must be ten or eleven inches long, you lucky woman. Almost enough for both of us. Not quite, so you'd better go catch another. But not now! He raised such a commotion all the other trout in the pool will be hiding and won't bite again for half an hour. I looked at her, flushed, breathless, and excited beyond measure, her brown eyes dancing. I can see her still, even though that happened fifty years ago and forty-five before she died. Only once have I seen her more beautiful and that was when she held our first child Cathy, in her arms at the hospital.

While we waited for the fish to calm themselves, she watched me clean the big trout. "See, it's easy," I said. "Just slit it below the gills sidewise, then slit it up the middle like this, then take your thumb and forefingers and strip out all the entrails with a single motion. No need to scale trout but you do have to take your thumbnail and scrape out the black blood on the inside of the backbone like this. Now let's put it back on the moss until I've built the cooking fire and have some coals, and until you catch a bigger one. But for now, just sit down on that log and look at that glorious orange and red U.P. sunset." Shakily, she did so as I built a little fire of dry driftwood between two logs.

"Oh, Cully," she exclaimed. "Now I can understand your love for trout fishing. It's the most exciting thing I've ever done. You'll never fish alone again." I rolled my eyes, remembering my father's words of wisdom.

As the fire burned down and we sat on the log with our arms around each other watching the western skies, the half-hour passed swiftly and she was out on the dam again. And soon she had caught another trout not as large as the first one, but at least nine inches long. This she cleaned herself, with only a few suggestions from me. "Now it's my turn," I said. I want to try fly fishing with your rod and I've seen some trout rising over there where the spring comes in. Dry the fish with this toilet paper, sprinkle salt all along the insides, and roll them in the flour that's in this little bag, then lightly salt again on the outside. You can use this slab of birchbark for a table. Cook them slowly in the frying pan until they're a deep brown outside, then call me when they're ready. Oh yes, fry the bacon first."

Unstringing the rod, I substituted another reel from my pocket that held a fly line, put on a new leader and attached a number sixteen caddis dry fly to its end. Walking along the shore to the foot of the pool, I then waded back upstream along a hidden sand bar almost to the snag. Once there I took several false casts to get the feel of the little rod, then let one cast carry the fly to a patch of foam where the eddy began. The fly lit perfectly for once and without any drag, when suddenly a big trout leaped out of the water and hit it on the way down. It too put up quite a fight on that little rod, once almost taking the line into some bushes, but I turned him back into the pool and soon had him in the net. It was larger than the one Milove had caught so I took out the hook and carefully slid the fish back into the pool. What a good moment! To be there at sunset in a lovely pool of clear water with a beautiful new wife waiting for me on shore with trout in the frying pan; well, it's a picture I've never forgotten. Resisting a temptation to try for another, I joined Milove. Yes, she had seen the whole thing. "How big was your trout?" she asked.

"Oh, not as large as yours," I lied happily. I see you had to cut the heads off yours so they'd fit in the pan. They'll be ready soon."

It was a memorable meal though I had to show her how to cut the skin lengthwise along the side, then flake off the pink meat, leaving the backbone intact. Even the korpua and coffee were very good, and before we left for camp I taught Milove how to do my Grampa Gage's Dance of the Wild Cucumber all along the bank.

One of the best days of my life!

THE LIE

Besides the stories, jokes and sayings that kept the tongues of Tioga wagging throughout the winter, we also had rumors that swept the village all year round. "They say that the new English teacher, Miss Young, doesn't wear any panties under her skirts." "I hear that the Northwestern Railroad is going to pull up its tracks to Michigamme." "Did you know that Bessie Siemen is pregnant with her fourteenth kid? Hope that won't be feebleminded too." "Hear tell that Joe Paquette come back from Lake Tioga with a forty-five pound pike. Probably netted it." "Someone told me the Jensons are selling their homestead and going to move to Republic." Every year or two when I was growing up a same rumor appeared: the Oliver Iron Mining Company was going to reopen the Tioga mine. "Yah, Charlie Schwartz, the telegrapher down at the depot, heard that from the one in Marquette who heard it from a man high up in Cleveland Cliffs who got it from someone in Duluth."

Unlike jokes which demand a certain consistency in the retelling, our rumors changed as they went up the hill or around the valley with so many revisions and embellishments that finally they were completely unlike the original. When Eric Niemi came to town after breakup one spring he asked Annie, our postmistress, if it was true that the Cleveland Cliffs had bought the Oliver Mining Company. Even if only one mouth had done the telling, the tale could change. Collecting tidbits of gossip on her daily rounds, Aunt Lizzie had heard from Mrs. Dusaine at the bottom of the hill that Andy Axelson had been seen making eyes at Marguerite, her daughter. By the time Aunt Lizzie visited Mrs. Christenson at the top of the hill she was saying that she'd heard that Andy had raped Marguerite in the Bellaire's haymow. Not that it mattered too much. No one believed Aunt Lizzie anyway, but the rumor was repeated just the same. Something to talk about over coffee.

Since this is the story about the ugliest rumor ever to raise hell in Tioga, I must tell you something about the people involved.

Henri Bonet had been a very strange child compared to other kids in Tioga. He never fought at all. Why, he'd even let much smaller boys beat him up. They called him "Goody-goody" or "Angel-face." He did have the face and disposition of an angel and Henri was smart too, always getting 100s on his report card - even in deportment. Unlike the rest of the village boys, he never went fishing or hunting or swimming. Certainly, he never played hooky. Instead, he usually hung around the Catholic church where he served as an acolyte and altar boy to Father Hassel, the parish priest. Not only on Sundays, Henri was also there after school on weekdays doing what he could to make himself useful because, as he told Father Hassel once, he wanted to become a priest too some day. The first of his class to master the catechism, he soon began to pick up some of the Latin phrases used in the liturgy and constantly pored over his little black bible, often asking the priest the meanings of many of the verses. Impressed by the boy's devotion and piety, Father Hassel encouraged Henri, gave him religious books to read, and soon found himself playing the role of a real father as well as a pastoral one.

One day when he discovered that Henri had cleaned and polished all the candlesticks without being told to do so, Father Hassel patted Henri on the head and said, Henri, you are a great comfort to an old man, my son. Yes, you are like a son to me." Henri began to weep. "But I'm not my own father's son," he said. "Mon pere, he don't like me at all. He spits on the floor when he sees me and makes a face. He doesn't want me to be a priest. He calls me a weak poulet (chicken), no son of his." The boy sobbed for a long time and then he told the priest how worried he was about his mother, that she had spells when she was very sick, when she could hardly breathe, when her face was covered with sweat and she would bang her heart place with her fist. "Has she been to see Dr. Gage?" the priest asked. "No," answered Henri. "Mon pere, he say no."

That afternoon Father Hassel came to our house to have his weekly chess game with my Dad and the usual glass of whiskey and one of the undertaker's good cigars. (Both my father and the priest got a box of those cigars from Mr. Stenrud every Christmas.) Occasionally, as they lifted their glasses, one would toast Mr. Stenrud: "First, the doctor;

106

then the priest; then the undertaker." But that afternoon, things were more serious as Father Hassel told Dad about Mrs. Bonet and asked him to call on her. "I'll pay your fee, Doctor. Her son, Henri is a treasure to me and he's greatly concerned." Dad told him of course he'd be glad to go and that the fee would be a mass for his benighted agnostic soul after he died. They were very good friends and always enjoyed each other.

When my father returned from seeing Henri's mother, he phoned Father Hassel. "She's in a bad way, Father," Dad said. "She has ventricular tachycardia, a heart disease characterized by episodes of heartbeats that race completely out of control. Mrs. Bonet had a minor attack when I was there and the pulse was so fast I couldn't count it, let alone feel it. She recovered but it's very probable that some time soon the heart muscle will go into fibrillation and that will be it. You'd better go down there and prepare them for her death. It could come any time. She'll be lucky to be alive a month from now."

Dad's prognosis was wrong for once. Henri's mother lived another year before the fibrillation took her. Henri was a sophomore in high school, taking his first course in Latin, when his world fell apart. His father gave him ten dollars and told him to get the hell out and make his own way in the world as he had done when he was fifteen. A married sister who lived in Tioga couldn't take him in so he could finish his schooling, so arrangements were made for him to live with an aunt in Marquette. In desperation Henri asked Father Hassel if he could live with him. "No, my son," the old priest said, "It is against the rules of the church." He wept as he said the words.

Not much was heard of Henri in the next years except that he changed from being an angel into a devil. In Marquette his aunt couldn't control him at all. He fought, got drunk, and even stole money from her until finally she showed him the door. Later, Annie said his sister had sent Henri a postal money order to a jail address in Milwaukee. Someone also said he'd gotten into trouble with the police in Detroit but didn't know the details. Henri finally did return to the U.P., however, because a little piece in the Marquette Mining Journal mentioned that a Henri Bonet, age 22, formerly of Tioga, had been arrested for aggravated assault and was being held in jail there awaiting trial.

When Father Hassel saw the item, he immediately took the train to Marquette to see what he could do to help. Entering the cell, he hardly recognized Henri at first and, when he tried to talk with him, Henri just turned his face to the wall. The priest conferred with the prosecuting attorney and the judge and hired a lawyer. In the end, Henri got off lightly because of the priest's efforts: one year in the county jail and a sentence of four more which would be suspended on condition that Father Hassel be held responsible for his good behavior. Henri had almost killed that man, they said, and would have done so if

107

bystanders had not pulled his hands off the man's throat.

Every Friday for the fifty-two weeks of the sentence Father Hassel went to Marquette to see his wayward son, and although at first the visits were most unpleasant and frustrating, by the end of that year much of their old relationship had been reestablished. When the jail door finally opened, Father Hassel was there to welcome Henri to a new life. The ladies of the Order of the Eastern Star had cleaned the old house, vacant since his father had died two years before, and they had a hot supper ready for the two of them. The priest told Henri that he was to go to the section house at seven next morning because he'd gotten him a job patrolling the railroad right-of-way by handcar. Joe Velain would be his partner and show him how to do the job. He said he hoped to see Henri at confession Saturday afternoon and at Mass on Sunday.

Well, everything turned out fine. Henri did well enough to be made foreman of another railroad maintenance crew. Remembering the terms of his probation, he never went to Higley's saloon nor did any fighting. After the second year, Henri married Fred Vachon's daughter, Michelle, and soon they had a son who was baptized by Father Hassel. Every week, Henri not only went to confession and mass but also visited the priest for conversation and to do odd chores for him. He loved the old man who had been so good to him and who had given him a new life.

That isn't the end of Henri's story, however. But first I must tell you about Sylvie Vautrin, certainly the ugliest woman in Tioga and perhaps the ugliest in the whole U.P. She was also Father Hassel's housekeeper and had been so for many years. Saying that Sylvie was ugly is an understatement. "Repulsive" might be a better word. Thin as a wagon spoke, when she walked she seemed to be crouching but it was her face that hit you hardest. The left side of it was colored by a huge red and purple birthmark that ran up into her straggly hair almost surrounding one eye. (Back then there was no cosmetic surgery and if you had a birthmark it stayed with you all your days.) The right half of Sylvie's face had no birthmark but there were several prominent moles, each with a tiny tuft of hair protruding from it. And she was hairy, hirsute beyond belief, with a visible brown mustache and arms covered with brown fuzz beyond her wrists to her knuckles. The word was that someone had seen her swimming naked once and that she even had hair on her breasts.

If these words seem cruel instead of factual (which they are), they simply reflect the cruelty of the god that formed her or perhaps the cruelty from others that she had known all her life. No one in Tioga ever looked at Sylvie when they met her on the street even if they politely said, "Bon Jour, Mamselle." When her parents went to church, they left Sylvie at home. When company came, she went to her bedroom. Her school years must have been terrible ones. I don't know;

I was too young to have known her then. Although she was smart and did well in school, she quit after the fourth grade to escape the cruelty of her peers and to help her mother with the washing and ironing of the clothes brought to them by the trainmen. Thereafter Sylvie remained invisible, almost forgotten by the village.

At that time, this was not unusual. Several families in Tioga had "hiddens", as we called them: a demented aunt, a grossly mentally retarded son, a severely crippled daughter. There were few social services. Except for the insane asylum in Newberry, there was literally no place to put the severely impaired, so we kept them hidden at home.

Sylvie was eighteen when a series of circumstances freed her from isolation and drudgery. A very young priest who had probably been assigned to Tioga for testing, or perhaps as a punishment for his rebellious behavior at the seminary, almost wrecked the parish. He was arrogant, made few pastoral calls, missed confessionals, didn't do the mass very well, and gave terribly severe penances for small sins. There were Sundays when only a handful of the faithful showed up in church. Finally when one evening he took the train for Chicago along with his housekeeper, all the parish sighed with relief and said "Good riddance."

His replacement was Father Hassel, a man who had served brilliantly as the deputy of the archbishop in Chicago and was being considered as a possible bishop when an opening would occur. However, when one did appear, Father Hassel refused. "I am too old," he protested. "I am tired of administration. Find me a little parish in some isolated village where I can tend my flock and really be a priest in my old age."

When the news came from Marquette that Tioga was getting a new priest, the parishioners got busy in a hurry. The church was scrubbed from stem to stern; the altar cloths washed and ironed; the candlesticks polished; the parsonage spruced up and ready for him. But they couldn't find a housekeeper. They searched and threatened and begged, but to no avail. Finally some one thought of Sylvie. "Non! Non!" said Pierre DuPont. "He take wan look for her an' take next train out!" Others disagreed. "Every priest should have an ugly housekeeper," one said. "Sylvie is smart; she can cook and clean; she will be grateful to get out of the closet and have her own money for once. If he is a holy man, he can bear how she looks." Nevertheless, they were greatly worried about how their new priest might react when he saw Sylvie, the horrible.

They needn't have been so concerned. Father Hassel accepted the situation easily. As he told my father once when Dad gently teased him about his ugly housekeeper, "I do not see faces, Doctor. I see souls."

Within two years Father Hassel changed his parish completely. Every Sunday the church was filled to capacity; so was the poor box. Father Hassel, unlike the other priests, never begged for money. He didn't need to. People gave all they could and then a bit more because they knew he cared for them not only when they were sick or dying, but even when they were well. A familiar sight on our hill street and back roads, he made his rounds daily. Even in the winter when the deep snows came and the wind blew cold, we would see Father Hassel plunging through the drifts, holding his cassock high above the boots and heavy wool pants he wore as he made his missions to the troubled of flesh or heart. Speaking to everyone he met in that deep calm voice, he made us all feel good. I remember feeling really blessed when once he stopped me, laid a big hand on my head, and held a brief conversation. Father Hassel loved little kids and often had an entourage of them as he went from house to house on his pastoral calls. French Canadians who hadn't been to confession or mass for years found their faith renewed when he sought them out in isolated cabins that had never seen a priest. Seeming to have no fear, my father sometimes would beg him not to enter a house that he had plastered with a quarantine sign bearing the big red letters of *"SCARLET FEVER"*. "No," said Father Hassel. "If you will enter to save their bodies, I will enter to save their souls." I have already told you how Henri adored the old priest. He was not alone.

One day during their chess game when Dad discovered that Father Hassel would soon be celebrating his 78th birthday, he organized a banquet of appreciation for his 18 years of services to the community. It would be held in the school gymnasium; there would be free food and speeches. Thanks not only to the Catholic ladies of the Order of the Eastern Star, but also to those of the Methodist and Swedish Lutheran Churches, it was a great success. Even Finns came, even some who would never eat the meat off the tail bone of a chicken because it was called "the pope's nose." Indeed, even the Finnish and Lutheran attended, and when the bishop from Marquette sang Father Hassel's praises, they applauded. Never had our little village felt so united.

That unity lasted only a few months. It was shattered when Sylvie became pregnant. Impossible! Oh, a few had noticed with approval that finally she had begun to put a little weight on that gaunt frame as she daily climbed and descended the hill street from the parsonage. Probably because she shared the good meals she cooked for the priest, they said. But when that weight seemed to get more concentrated, tongues began to wag. Then one day, when Sylvie was seen going to my father's hospital at office hour time, and then that night boarding the train to Green Bay where her sister lived, all hell broke loose.

Sylvie pregnant? What man, no matter how drunk, would touch her? Who was the father of that unborn child? Could it have been the priest? NO! That was incredible. And yet...

Oh, the ugly rumors! Oh, the vicious gossip! Father Hassel was too old. But was he? Old man Vattila had fathered a child by his second young wife at the age of 89. No, that didn't mean anything. Vattila just had good neighbors. But Father Hassel was a truly good man. He wouldn't do such hanky-panky. He was a wise man; he'd have too much sense. And yet? Who else might have done it? How about that feeble minded moron, Willie Martel? No, he'd been cookee in Silverthorne's logging camp all winter. Who else?

So far as Father Hassel was concerned, nothing seemed to have changed. Benevolently he cared for his people, his face calm and peaceful. Some of them wondered if he had even heard any of the cruel gossip. Until a new housekeeper could be found, Mrs. Bussiere and other women took weekly turns cooking and cleaning for him up at the parsonage. Life went on very smoothly. The whole matter would soon be forgotten.

But that was only on the surface. Beneath it were doubt and evil thoughts. When Antoine Bizet remarked regarding Pere Hassel that "En la nuit toutes les chats sont gris" (At night all cats are gray), his neighbor threw an axe at him. An old Finnish saying swept the town: "Once you get them 'neath the blankets, all women are the same." When Aunt Lizzie who, for all her faults, feared God but no man, came to my father's office and asked him point blank if he'd found Sylvie pregnant and if the priest was the father, Dad grabbed her by the scruff of the neck and literally kicked her down the hospital steps. At supper he was still so furious I didn't even dare ask him to pass the butter.

Uptown, innuendos, slurs, and nasty little jokes about the Catholics were passed from one Finn house to another. For the older ones, the happening merely corroborated what they had always known about the Catholics and their priests. After school the Finn and French kids slugged it out. Even in the woods, the young men fought. Joe Pitou and Andy Avila, who had been friends for years, beat each other to a pulp when Andy, referring to Father Hassel, had spoken the word "father" with a certain intonation.

The worst of these fights occurred in the post office and involved Henri Bonet who should have remembered that he still had a year to go on his probation. Henri had come to mail his wife's letter to her sister in Hancock when, entering the door, he heard Untu Pekkari and a friend laughing, and Untu saying something about Father Hassel and reciting "The holy pole is in your hole so wiggle your ass to save your soul."

Of course Henri jumped him, got him down on the floor and began choking Untu until his face was turning blue, just as he had done to that other man four years earlier. When they broke his throat grip, Henri began to weep, then straightened up and said very slowly "Father Hassel is a saint. He wasn't the one who knocked up Sylvie. It was me! I tell you it was me and if Sylvie comes back with child I will adopt it and make it my own. Say no more about my priest."

Within the hour the news of what Henri had said swept the valley and the furthest Finn houses uptown. It had even preceded him to his own house where he found Michelle rocking their little son and weeping bitterly. Henri could not talk; he just wept too.

It was three weeks before Henri could bring himself to go to confession and when he did, he said nothing about Sylvie. Father Hassel gently urged him to say more and then urged him again. "I have heard, my son, what you have told about my housekeeper. Surely you can tell me."

Henri was silent for a long time before he spoke. "Father," he said, "As you may or may not know, I lied."

GOING BACK TO
THE U.P.

Tom Hedet's boy-hood in Tioga had been a wonderful experience and he'd loved every moment of it. Roaming the forest, fishing the lakes and streams, yes, even going to school had been good, but when he entered his senior year in high school the future didn't look so promising. It was 1931, the depth of the Great Depression.

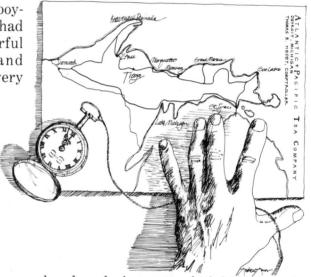

Banks had failed; mines were closed or closing; every freight train had a boxcar full of hopeless, homeless men searching for a place where some job might be available. Cars loaded with pulp sat on the railroad siding because there was no market for it. No one had biting money.

Tom saw that he, like many others, would have to leave Tioga and the U.P. Perhaps in the cities Down Below there would be an opportunity to make a living. He didn't want to go. He wanted to live in the U.P. all his life, to raise a family there so his children could have the joys he'd had.

Taking stock of himself, he tried to decide what kind of work he'd want to do the rest of his life, what his assets and liabilities were. Well, he'd always been especially good in mathematics. Maybe he'd become a mathematics teacher in some high school. But that didn't appeal to him. Teachers never made much money and they had to spend a lot of time disciplining. He didn't want to grow up to be like Old Blue Balls, no sir! What he'd really like would be a job in business or a business of his own so he could make a lot of money, retire early, and come back to spend the rest of his days in the U.P.

So Tom came up to our house to see my father for advice. "Work your way through college," said Dad. "I did, and you can too. I clerked for a year in a hotel doing bookkeeping, taught a year in a country school, worked in a bank as a teller and bookkeeper, oh a lot of things, but I got an education and became a doctor that way. Times are tough right now but they'll get better, so prepare yourself for them. Go to school. Go to the University of Michigan and become an accountant. If you want to have a business of your own you've got to learn how to keep books."

Dad also made arrangements with Mr. Flynn so that he would teach Tom how to keep the store's books, if he'd work without pay and just for the experience. Mr. Flynn told Dad later that Tom was a natural, that he was very good at figures, was well organized, and had been a lot of help once he'd learned the ropes.

The day following his high school graduation Tom spent in walking all the streets of Tioga, swimming in Fish Lake off Big Rock, and catching a mess of trout up in the Escanaba. He was homesick already. But the next morning he started hitchhiking to Ann Arbor with fifty dollars in his pockets from the family sugar bowl. "It's a loan," his father told him, "and it comes hard, so pay it back as soon as you can." His mother made him some sandwiches and wiped some of her tears. Tom wiped some too.

The hitchhiking took three days and after paying the fare to cross on the ferry at the Straits, he arrived in Ann Arbor still with forty-two dollars and a bad case of homesickness. Then, armed with a "To Whom It May Concern" recommendation from Mr. Flynn, Tom made the rounds of all the businesses on State Street hunting for a job. Finally he found one at Wahr's bookstore. No, they didn't need a full-time bookkeeper but they were taking inventory now that the University was not in session, and if he did well they would pay him fifteen dollars a week for as long as the job lasted. Tom also soon got another job as a janitor, sweeping and cleaning one of the classroom buildings from six P.M. until two in the morning, which paid forty dollars a month. Then a nice old lady rented him an attic room with a cot and a chair and a table for twenty dollars a month. Food, however, seemed terribly expensive and all that first year Tom lived on day-old bakery bread, peanut butter and strawberry jam. Although he saved every penny, he found in the fall that he had only enough to pay for matriculation and two courses at the university, neither of which were in business. No matter! He was on his way. Someday he'd have his own business, make a lot of money, and get back to the U.P.

It took Tom six years instead of four to graduate from the U of M business school, six tough years of holding two and sometimes three jobs. Throughout that time he found himself constantly dreaming of the U.P. and Tioga. Someday he'd fish the headwaters beyond the Haysheds. Sometime he'd sit again under that waterfall on the east branch. Sometime he'd smell arbutus again. Often it was hard to study.

He almost got back there at the end of his third year. A student had an old Model-T Ford he wanted to sell for only thirty dollars. It was in bad shape inside and out but the owner said it ran fine, so Tom, against his good judgment, bought the thing. He had a week of vacation after classes had ended, not enough to get home hitchhiking, but enough if he drove all night. He got only as far as Clare where a garage mechanic told him the block was cracked and he needed a new motor, that it would cost at least one hundred and fifty dollars. Tom left it and his dreams there and made his way back to Ann Arbor.

Again, after he had graduated he planned to take a few weeks off before beginning the new job that he'd been offered. A good job. He'd be a junior accountant at the headquarters of the Atlantic and Pacific Tea Company in Detroit. Good pay and fine possibilities for advancement. Tom wrote his parents telling them the good news and saying he'd be with them the last week of June. For a week he pictured to himself all the thing he'd do. Then he got a special delivery letter saying that they'd sold the house and were moving to Marinette, Wisconsin. They wouldn't be there in Tioga but would love to have him come see them in their new home. Instead Tom went to Detroit to find a place to live. Would he ever get back to Tioga? Where would he stay if he did?

For the first six months Tom found the new job fascinating as he mastered the various skills involved. Mr. Phillipson, the senior accountant, was a good boss, always willing to help or explain, and better yet, to forgive when Tom made the inevitable mistakes of a beginner. Oh, there were some things about the job that he didn't like. Sitting all day at a desk in a large room full of other desks, poring over papers, doing the same things over and over again. Moreover he hated the city. Too many people; too much noise; everyone in a hurry! Tom resented the morning and evening hassle of taking the streetcars to and from work. He'd found a good room in the suburbs but that meant a forty minute ride each way. On weekends he was often lonely and going to the zoo or a museum didn't help much. There were always crowds there too. Tioga had no crowds. Tom found himself doing a lot of daydreaming about the U.P.

After the holidays, the daydreaming increased. *Accounts payable:* A huge stack of them arrived every day on his desk for him to sort, organize and enter. (How deep would the snow be in Tioga now? Would the drifts cover the fence around the old school? Would the snow squeak under your footsteps?) *Account receivable:* (Remember how we made that ski jump in Company Field? Are the ravens till croaking as they soar over The Grove?) *Cash payments:* (They'll probably have a basketball game tonight in the Town Hall: the Michigamme versus Tioga town teams. There'll be some good fights and maybe a howl or two if some player brushes against the potbellied stove. *Cash receipts:* (How good it was to have breakup time in the spring. Remember how we made snow dams across the hill street? Remember that first arbutus? The pink kind always smelled more fragrant than the white.) *Posting and vouchers:* (Fishing for trout in the rapids; cowslips and marsh marigolds in the swamps; eating the new shoots of wild raspberries with salt.) *Trial balances:* (Tapping the big maple trees and driving in the spigots made from hollowed-out elderberry branches; sap icicles; maple sugar wax on new snow.) *Inventory Checking:* (Swimming in Tioga Lake when the great ice cake still floats in the middle of it; partridge drumming on a hollow log; sunsets and sunrises.) Yes, there were many times when Tom found it hard to concentrate on his work.

Nevertheless, after just two years he received a promotion to be a senior accountant with his own office and a secretary. Now he had to supervise several junior accountants and various clerks, prepare financial statements of profits and losses, balance sheets, and work out budgets. There were times when he was so busy he almost forgot there was an Upper Peninsula. Also he was studying hard to prepare for the C.P.A. examinations, because he knew that unless he became licensed as a certified public accountant, his career upward would be blocked. Having had to work so hard during his university days, his grades had only been Cs and Bs and there was much he had missed, but by studying hard evenings and weekends Tom finally passed all four parts of that tough examination. It paid off because soon he was promoted to be a chief accountant with a big boost in salary.

After three more years, Tom Hedet had a house, a new car, and a pregnant wife. He'd almost made it back to the U.P. for their honeymoon. The planning of that honeymoon had been fun. Having read a lot of books about the U.P., he'd sketched out the route. They'd spend the first night in St. Ignace, then drive to the Soo to watch the ships going through the canal. From there they'd visit the Tahquamenon Falls and spend the second night either in Grand Marais or Munising. The third night they'd be in a hotel in Marquette or Ishpeming and use that as a base from which they'd visit Tioga and all his old haunts. Then they'd go to L'Anse, the Keweenaw Peninsula, and over to Ironwood, and finally back to the Straits on US-2, along the shore of Lake Michigan, stopping in to see the great spring by Manistique. Oh, there was so much to see and do on that honeymoon!

But his new bride insisted on going to Niagara Falls instead.

In 1958 Tom Hedet was forty-five years old when they promoted him to be Comptroller of the company. Yes, his rise up the corporate ladder had been swift, almost meteoric, but Tom had paid the price. Now living in a big house in Bloomfield Hills, he had three children: Tom, Jr. aged 14; Jack 12 and Lisa 8. The trouble was that he hardly knew them. Oh, he gave them everything they wished including a new swimming pool, everything but his time. Each night he came home from the office with a brief case full of the work he would have to do that night. Often his weekends meant a day back at work. He ate too much and too fast, his wife said. He was too heavy and wheezed now when he climbed the stairs up to the bedroom where he slept fitfully when he slept at all. Of late he'd been very irritable, his wife told him. Well, he'd change now that he'd been made Comptroller. He'd take it easier and start having some fun with his kids. Yes, if he did an extra good job, they would probably make him Vice President in charge of financial services, but it was time to quit sacrificing his family and begin enjoying life. Lord, he hadn't had a real vacation in twenty-eight years. It was about time - about time he went back to Tioga and its lovely lakes and streams and forests. Forty-five wasn't really old, but there were times when he felt he was.

So Tom Hedet asked for and received a month's vacation before assuming his new duties. Then he bought one of the new travel trailers with all the conveniences, big enough for the whole family and then some. They would take the honeymoon he'd never had, cover the U.P. from stem to stern, see all the sights, and camp at Lake Tioga (where he'd heard they now had a State Park) for as long as they wished. Perhaps he'd take the camper up the river road to the Haysheds and catch a trout or two in that lovely pool below the old logging dam. Or let the kids catch some and cook them over an open fire at twilight. Oh, it would be good going back and being a boy again. Of course his old house would be there with some other family in it and there would be other changes, but perhaps he could find a cottage on Lake Tioga to buy for a summer or retirement home. Just the same he was going back, day after tomorrow, finally going back. He'd have to make just one more trip to the office to arrange for the switchover to his new suite of offices.

But Tom Hedet never did go back to Tioga. They found him slumped over his desk, dead. A massive heart attack! Probably never knew what hit him, the doctor said.

I guess the moral is obvious. To you who live in the U.P., cherish our lovely land. To you who don't, what the hell are you waiting for?

NOT YET

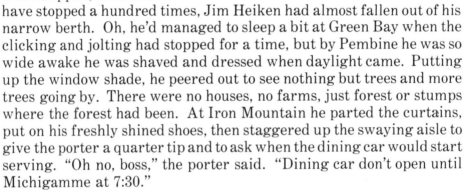

It had been a hard night on the sleeping car from Chicago. Every time the train stopped, and it must have stopped a hundred times, Jim Heiken had almost fallen out of his narrow berth. Oh, he'd managed to sleep a bit at Green Bay when the clicking and jolting had stopped for a time, but by Pembine he was so wide awake he was shaved and dressed when daylight came. Putting up the window shade, he peered out to see nothing but trees and more trees going by. There were no houses, no farms, just forest or stumps where the forest had been. At Iron Mountain he parted the curtains, put on his freshly shined shoes, then staggered up the swaying aisle to give the porter a quarter tip and to ask when the dining car would start serving. "Oh no, boss," the porter said. "Dining car don't open until Michigamme at 7:30."

Jim consulted his timetable. Two more stops at Sagola and Republic and then Tioga at 6:30. Tioga! The name had a good ring to it. It was where he'd live until next summer as their new high school math and science teacher. His first job! Hoped he could handle it. Jim reread the letter he'd received from the superintendent. 'Dear Mr. Heiken: Although school will not open until Monday, September 3rd, you should be here at least by the Saturday before, so we can get acquainted and I can outline your duties. After some difficulty, I have been able to arrange room and board for you at Mrs. Lizzie Campton's house for which you will pay thirty dollars a month. I shall be either at home or at the school and I'm sure someone will be able to direct you there. Sincerely, E.K. Aronson, Superintendent of Schools.'

Finally the train pulled in at the Tioga Station. As Jim descended the steps, he looked around. Where was the town? The business district? All he could see was a road ascending a huge hill on his left lined sparsely with houses and big maple trees. Perhaps it was on the other side of the depot. No, again all he saw were dirt roads with some whitewashed log cabins along them and a larger frame building beside the tracks which bore the sign "Higley's Saloon" on its false front. He went to the ticket window and stood there for some time watching a man with a green head visor tapping and listening to a bank of telegraph keys. Finally the clattering stopped and the man came to the window.

"Could you tell me where I could find a restaurant, please?" Jim asked. "They weren't serving breakfast on the train from Chicago."

"Naw!" said the man. "You come seven years too late. That's when the mine closed and so did the cafe and the hotel and the boarding house. You the new science teacher for the high school?"

"Yes, my name's Jim Heiken. I'm to meet Mr. Aronson this morning to find out what I have to do. Can you tell me how I can find his house?"

"Why sure," said the telegrapher. "You just climb the hill street past the new school. His house is the big yellow and brown one just opposite the Methodist church. Let's see. It's Saturday. Eskil will be having his breakfast about eight o'clock, it not being a school day, so maybe you could get a cup of coffee there if you time it right. He and his wife are good people, the Aronsons are. Not like Old Blue Balls who used to be our super. Why don't you leave your bag here and look around the valley? We got a lot of French Canadians and Indians down here back of the station and uptown you'll find the Finns and Cousin Jacks and such. Why don't you go see the old iron smelter furnace and the waterfall? Cross the tracks and take the road to the left, but don't go up the hill."

Jim thanked him and did so. On his way a little girl said hello and a bit further two old men were leaning against a fence talking French. When he said good morning to them they smiled and said, "Bon Jour, Msieu." Then one said, "I think you be ze new high school teachair, oui? You like it here. We got fine new school now." Well, thought Jim, the natives were sure friendly. Despite the gnawing in his stomach, he was beginning to feel good, and the old furnace and waterfall were sure picturesque. By the time he returned to the depot to pick up his bag it was a quarter to eight.

The hill street was even steeper than it looked and Jim's arm was almost ready to fall off from carrying his bag when he came upon the school on his left. It was impressive. A large brick two-story building set upon a knoll surrounded by a large schoolyard, it looked very new. Just beyond it at the steepest part of the hill he'd yet encountered, he also found the Methodist-Episcopal church and across from it the superintendent's house. He pulled out his watch, and since it read 8:15 Jim climbed the steps to the porch and knocked on the door.

The Aronsons, as the telegrapher had predicted, were having breakfast and insisted that he join them. Oatmeal with wild blueberries smothered with thick yellow cream, it was accompanied by a curious cold hard toast that they called korpua. When Mrs. Aronson poured Jim a cup of coffee and Jim refused, saying that he'd never learned to drink it yet, they both insisted that he do so. "You'll soon find that in Tioga they always offer you coffee the moment you step inside the door," Mrs. Aronson said. "And if you refuse, they'll be insulted." Her husband nodded and grinned. "Yes, that's right, Jim. You'll discover a lot of odd customs in this out-of-the-way place. Have you ever had a sauna?"

"No, what's a sauna?"

"A steam bath. All the Finns go sauna every Saturday night and sometimes even during the week. They're a very clean people. It will be an experience the first time. By the way, do you have enough money to pay Mrs. Campton in advance for your room and board? If you don't I'll lend you some till pay day." When Jim said that he had fifty dollars in his wallet, Mr. Aronson said that would be enough and that he'd walk with him up to her house.

As they did so, Mr. Aronson pointed out my Dad's hospital and the boarded-up Beacon House with its long veranda. "Until the mine suddenly closed after the cave-in, Tioga must have been quite a little city," the Superintendent said. "Had its own hotel, fire department, club house, and there's the boarding house where the miners without families lived. The building next to it is Flynn's store where you can still buy anything. By the way, I suggest you buy a felt hat or cap, Jim, as soon as you can. I know that Down Below and in Chicago all the men wear straw hats like yours, but up here they'll poke fun at you and think you're a sissy for wearing one and knock it off your head perhaps. Just look carefully inside the hat to make sure there aren't any lice. That big building across from the store is our Town Hall where town meetings are held. It's also our jail. We also have a little village library upstairs in it that is open on Thursday afternoons and evenings. Not many books in it though."

They met several tow-headed children whom Mr. Aronson greeted by name and an old lady with whom he stopped for a brief conversation after introducing the new teacher. "Always say hello to every person you meet," the superintendent advised, "and tell them who you are and how much you like our town even if you don't. It's a custom. Oh yes, and watch your feet when walking on this board sidewalk. The cows and horses roam up and down our street freely and you have to dodge their manure. Not like Chicago, is it?" He grinned.

Just before they came to Easy Street where Mrs. Campton lived, the superintendent told Jim a bit about her. "We call her Aunt Lizzie and she's quite a character, to put it mildly. She's the town gossip and not a nice one either. I really didn't want to have you board with her but I couldn't for the life of me find any other place. Perhaps we can later if you just can't stand her yakking, but she's a fine cook and will put some meat on those bones of yours." Jim was a bit surprised when they went to the back rather than the front door. "That's another of our customs," Mr. Aronson said. "Front doors are for funerals."

Mrs. Campton came to the door when they knocked. A tall, rawboned woman with a sharp nose and jaw, she was holding a tiny Pekinese dog who kept barking. "Hush now, Sweetie Pie," she said to it as Mr. Aronson introduced Jim. "I know you don't like nasty men but he's our new boarder so shush!" The Superintendent didn't stay long. "Drop in at the school after dinner, Jim, and I'll show you around and tell you your duties," he said as he departed.

Mrs. Campton sat Jim down at the kitchen table. "Well?" Her voice was as sharp as her nose. "You must pay in advance, young man. Do you have towels and soap?" Jim shook his head. "Well, I'll furnish them then and do your laundry for five dollars extra a month, so it will be thirty-five dollars right now. You'll have to iron your own shirts though."

When Jim paid her the money, Aunt Lizzie took him upstairs. Like the kitchen, the little bedroom was spotless - too spotless. It held only a large bed, a small table with a kerosene lamp, and two chairs, one a sagging stuffed purple monster. Also there was a commode with pitcher, basin and slop jar. That was all. Jim asked about the bathroom and when she led him to it all he saw was an empty claw-footed bathtub without faucets. No toilet! Aunt Lizzie saw his puzzlement. "I don't have running water," she explained. "If you want to take a bath, you'll have to bring up teakettles of hot water from the kitchen or have a sauna over at Mrs. Kutinen's house next door. They heat it every Saturday and only charge ten cents. As for the toilet, you'll use the outhouse out back by the barn or the slop jar. And mind you, you'll have to empty and clean it every time. I keep a clean house, Mr. Heiken. Leave your bag up here and come down to the kitchen for a cup of coffee and I'll tell you the rules."

There were a lot of them. No hanky-panky. No visitors, no women! He would have to make his bed before he left in the morning. Breakfast, dinner and supper were at seven, twelve and six on the dot. No tracking mud into the kitchen. No, he couldn't play the organ except when she asked him to. He could come downstairs and sit in the kitchen with her, but only if she gave permission. He had to be nice to Lulubelle. There were a lot more of those rules before Jim fled upstairs to unpack.

After doing so, he decided to wash up but found no water in the pitcher, and when he asked Aunt Lizzie for some, she told him to get a pailful from the well outside. Jim took the pail but when he got to the well beside the woodshed he didn't know what to do. There was a rope and windlass but when he lowered the pail it just floated and wouldn't fill. Aunt Lizzie who'd been watching him through the kitchen curtains finally came out and showed him how to gather up the rope loosely, then plunge the pail upside down into the water. "Lordamighty," she said contemptuously, "you city folks don't even know how to get a pail of water from the well. On your way back, bring in an armful of small wood to make up for that I've used to heat your teakettle." Jim sure felt intimidated.

The noon meal, however, was very good: swiss steak, mashed potatoes and a fine apple pie. As Mr. Aronson had told him, his landlady was an excellent cook. Jim devoured the food but only between his answers to constant questions and Lulubelle's nipping at his ankles under the table. Finally he got away and en route to the school he bought a felt hat at Flynn's store. No lice!

The superintendent proudly showed him around the building. "It's as fine a school as you'll find in the U.P.," he said. "Although Tioga is a poor town, when the company suddenly closed the mine down and pulled up the railroad tracks, they forgot a large ore pile on the surface and the taxes on it are paying for the school. No, we're not hurting for money. We even provide free textbooks. Here, I'll get you copies of your texts. You'll teach algebra, geometry, trigonometry and physics and be in charge of the study hall when you aren't teaching. Later, look over your laboratories and see what other things you might need. We alternate physics and chemistry every other year and this year it's physics. I think we're well equipped." Mr. Aronson led the way to the teachers' room where he showed Jim his locker and then to the gymnasium downstairs. "I hope you know something about basketball because you'll have to coach our boy's team. It's our one sport and the town goes crazy if we can beat Michigamme or Republic. We'll pay you twenty dollars extra for each of the months you coach, from October to March." Jim told him he'd played the game in high school and would enjoy coaching. "But can you tell me something about the school policies concerning discipline," he asked. "This is my first teaching job and I'll need some guidance in a lot of things."

"Most of the discipline problems are in the lower grades," the superintendent replied. "Most of the troublemakers have quit school to work in the bush by the time they get to high school. There's one, Toivo Maki, who may give you a bad time because he wants to quit and his folks won't let him. All the students will have to test you, of course. Just start by being very tough and businesslike. You can always ease up later. Have them call you Mr. Heiken, never Jim, and learn their names as quickly as you can. Don't ever be sarcastic! Make your classes interesting and if you assign homework, make it brief. These kids all have a lot of chores to do when they get home from school. Let me see a lesson plan for one of your classes each day for about a month and expect me to visit your room to watch you teach occasionally. I won't be there the first couple of weeks, though. Come see me if you have any problems. Oh, by the way, you aren't ever to go to Higley's saloon or to the poolroom. Have to be a model, you know. Well, I'll see you at seven-thirty Monday morning in the teachers' room for a brief meeting with the other teachers."

Supper at Mrs. Campton's was also good: baked hash with an egg on top and some of the leftover pie. When Jim hesitantly asked if he could have milk instead of coffee, Aunt Lizzie told him he could but would have to pay an extra dollar a week if he wanted it with his meals. Then she asked him if he planned to go to the sauna, it being Saturday night. Jim demurred. "I had a bath last night just before getting on the train," he said defensively. Then came a long interrogation about his religious beliefs and affiliation. "You have to go to church," she told him. "All teachers are supposed to go to church. You aren't Catholic, I hope." No, Jim told her, he'd been brought up to be a Presbyterian but hadn't gone to church much in his college years. "Well, I'll take you with me to my church," she said. "It's Methodist Episcopal, the one near the school. We have Finnish Lutheran, Swedish Lutheran, Catholic and Holy Jumper churches, but the Methodist comes closest to Presbyterian, I think." For a moment Jim though of rebelling before finally he agreed to go with her. She sure was bossy!

Needing some exercise, that evening he walked up the road, there being no sidewalks, to the abandoned mine and spent a long time watching the swallows circling above the tall chimney, then plunging down into it. Some kids came to a fence to watch him walk by and a few lace curtains fluttered as he passed but he met no other person. How would he spend his waking hours when he wasn't in school? Suddenly he felt very much alone.

The next morning after breakfast Jim studied the textbooks he would have to use until it was time to go to church. When he came down from his room Aunt Lizzie looked him over critically. "You've got to shine your shoes," she said. "I don't have any shoe polish but I'll get you a cloth and some lard. School teachers always have to have their shoes polished." Jim complied and down the hillstreet they went. Aunt Lizzie talked all the way about all of the families who lived on the street. "The Hall sisters live there. They fight like cats and dogs, pulling hair and scratching till the blood comes. Old Mrs. Beatty lives there. She's batty with old age. In the brown house live the Hendersons. Four boys, no girls, but her father hung himself when Millie was born. Wanted a son and got six girls. Millie's made up for it. Has four boys. That's Dr. Gage's hospital and he lives in the house across from it. He doesn't like me and I don't know why. Has a boy Cully, who stammers. Probably be in one of your classes so don't ask him to recite." So it went until they got to the church where she wanted him to sit in the front pew but he insisted on sitting in the back, a decision he regretted when he found the parishioners turning around to look at him and whispering among themselves.

The sermon was long and dull but the congregation lustily sang many of the old hymns that he knew. Jim had a bit of a problem getting up and down because the varnish on the pews was a bit sticky, but all in all it was a bearable experience - except when Aunt Lizzie, who sang soprano in the choir, hit some of the high notes way off key. He noted with a bit of amusement that the organist tried to drown her out but the louder she played, the louder Aunt Lizzie screeched. After the service, among many introductions, he met the organist. "I'm Annie Anderson, the postmistress," she said. "I'll have a box ready for you, Jim, but the Chicago mail won't be disturbed until eight o'clock so you'll probably have to pick it up when you come home from school." How did she already know that he came from Chicago? Jim was soon to learn that in Tioga everyone knew everything about everybody.

The next morning the teachers' meeting was brief. Mr. Aronson walked into it with Jim and introduced him to the eleven teachers already there. "I see that you've already met Ruth Keski, our new seventh grade teacher," he said to them. "Her home is in the Soo and she has her life certificate from the Normal School in Marquette. This is Jim Heiken who will teach math and science for us. He hails from the University of Chicago. Both Ruth and Jim are first year teachers, so I hope you'll help them all you can over the first rough weeks. I'll pass out your class rolls now. If there are additions or deletions, please let me know and be sure to tell me when there are more than two consecutive unexcused absences. Just one other thing: students this year may not be in the classrooms until the first bell rings. You'll recall that we had some problems last year about that. Let's have a fine good year." That was all.

Before the teachers left for their classrooms, Jim looked them over. Except for Ruth they were all women in their forties or fifties, veterans of many years of coping with children. The new one, Ruth, seemed very young and not particularly attractive with her horn-rimmed glasses and blonde hair swept back into a tight bun. Probably Finnish. Jim wished that there had been at least one other male. Well, all of them seemed pleasant enough.

His classes went well enough except that he had a lot of trouble when calling the roll, soon learning from the pupils' laughter that Delongchamp was pronounced "Delosha" and Deroche was "Derushy." Ysitalo was not "Yess-o-tolo" but "Issatalo." They were otherwise well-behaved and seemed interested in his explanation of the course contents. He gave each of them a first assignment: to write a one-page summary of who they were and what their interests were so he could become acquainted. The day went swiftly but he found he was very tired when it ended. Although it was fascinating and fun, teaching was hard work too.

However, as the month of September passed, Jim found himself becoming more depressed and miserable than he'd ever been in his whole life. It wasn't the teaching. That was the best part with its constant challenges, but once school was out for the day he just didn't

124

know what to do with his empty time. He'd walked all the streets of the village and taken the back road to Lake Tioga several times. Once he'd picked up rock specimens at the old mine and visited the little town library on Thursday evening when it was open, hoping to find a book on geology so he could identify the samples, but there was no such book. Afraid to venture into the deep woods, he felt imprisoned. Hungering for male companionship, he once introduced himself to some younger men at the post office intending to ask them who might rent him a boat so he could row out to the islands on the big lake. "I'm Jim Heiken," he said. "I'm the new math and science teacher, and..." That's as far as he got. They coldly looked him over and said, "Is that so?" and walked away. He even thought of asking Ruth, the new seventh grade teacher for a date, but where would they go? To see the evening train pull out of the depot? No movie, no dances, no nothing! There was absolutely nothing to do in Tioga.

Life at Aunt Lizzie's house became almost unbearable. She talked and questioned him until he couldn't stand it. She also exploited him, asking him to do this and that. One Saturday morning, she came in and begged him to lend her a hand in cleaning out the chicken coop. "I'm a poor old widow woman," she'd said, "and I don't have my old strength any more," but as soon as she'd put the shovel in his hand she left for one of her gossip collecting trips down the street. "Will you chop some wood for me?" "Will you help me beat the carpets?" "Will you please fetch some more water from the well?" One day Jim rebelled. "No!," he almost shouted. "I pay for my room and board. I'm not your choreboy!" It didn't do any good. Aunt Lizzie didn't bat an eye, and soon she was demanding he do other things for her. It was her voice, that rasping whine, that almost drove him up the wall. And that damned dog, Lulubelle, always nipping at his ankles or yipping constantly even when it was out in the yard. He could hear her even when he was up in his little room sitting in the sagging purple chair trying to prepare a lesson for the following day. There was nothing to do if he left the house and just plain misery when he was in it! When the high school classes were dismissed for two days because it was potato picking time, Jim almost went nuts. Weekends also were always bad because they meant having to go to church with Aunt Lizzie,. Once he asked Ruth if he might attend the Finnish Lutheran church with her. "No," she answered. "That would mean that we were engaged to be married and I don't think either of us is quite ready for that yet. It would be like asking me to go sauna with you."

"Yet?" Hey, maybe behind those horned-rimmed glasses there might be somebody interesting. Oh nuts! To hell with her and to hell with Tioga! Why had he ever left Chicago?

Things kept getting worse and by the time he got his first paycheck on September 25th (schoolteachers always get that first check early because school boards know they're broke after the summer), Jim had decided to quit. The thought of paying Aunt Lizzie about a third of that

125

check for another month's misery was unendurable, so he told **Mr.** Aronson he was resigning. The superintendent didn't seem surprised but he asked for a few days to see if he couldn't find another place for him to live. "You're a fine teacher, Jim, and I'd sure hate to lose you. All of us know Aunt Lizzie and having to live with her nastiness must be hard, so I don't blame you a bit. I really didn't want to put you up with her but could find no other place then. Now I'll try again. Just give me a few more days." Jim agreed.

Two days later the superintendent called Jim into his office. "I've a place for you that ought to be fine, Jim," he said. "Mrs. Salmi has agreed to give you room and board until the end of school next May. You know her son, John. He's a senior this year and will probably be captain of the basketball team. I think he's in your physics class, isn't he?" Jim nodded and Mr. Aronson continued, "You can move in this afternoon after school if you want to. Ask John to go with you when you get your bags from Aunt Lizzie's and he'll show you where his house is. You'll like it there. No better woman in town than Mrs. Salmi. Her husband is away. He's on the crew of a diamond drilling outfit that travels all over the world hunting for iron ore, and right now he's in South America somewhere. You'll be in a typical Finnish home and have to eat what they eat and do as they do, but I think you'll enjoy every moment of it. Anyway, give it a try."

Aunt Lizzie wasn't home when Jim and John Salmi went to get his bag so he left her a little note and a five dollar bill just in case she had thought of something else he owed. Lord, was he glad to get out of there! Restraining an urge to give the yapping Lulubelle a kick, he sat down at the forbidden organ to honk a farewell.

The Salmi's house was about a quarter mile up a side road in a cluster of houses that was called Finn Town. Each had a wide yard, a cowbarn, garden, outhouse and chicken coop. Some of the houses including the Salmi's also had a log sauna. When they entered the back door and John introduced Jim, Mrs. Salmi welcomed him warmly. A large smiling woman wearing a white apron, she'd just taken some loaves of bread from the oven. "This morning," she said, "I just have iksi poika (one boy); now I have koksi (two), Yonny and Yimmy." She held both his hands and pumped them vigorously. "Don't call me Mrs. Salmi. Call me aiti (mother) like Yonny does. Yonny, you show Yimmy where he sleep and I then give you new leipa (bread) when you come down." John led the way upstairs to the bedrooms. "I'll keep the lower bunk, Mr. Heiken, and you take the top one." The room was spotless.

"Around here, Johnny, don't call me Mr. Heiken" Jim told him. "Call me Jim, though of course in school you'll have to use the Mister." What a change! What a change! It sure had been tough living at Aunt Lizzie's. When they came down, Mrs. Salmi gave them thick slices of the new buttered bread powdered with sugar and cinnamon and mugs of milk. Jim got the crust. She was beaming.

That whole weekend was an utter delight. On Saturday morning after John had done his chores, they dug a few worms and walked the woods trail to Fish Lake, caught a few little perch for bait, then sat on Big Rock fishing for Northern Pike. Jim's big bobber went down once but he struck too soon and missed the fish. "You have to let them have it a long time," John told him. It didn't matter. It was just good to sit there on the shore of a lovely lake watching the last brown leaves swirling on the surface. John knew so many things about the woods that a whole new world was opened for Jim. On their way back, the scuffling of their feet in the fallen leaves jumped a deer and flushed a partridge. "I'll ask Ma if I can use my Dad's Winchester pump gun and you can use my singleshot and we'll go hunting next weekend," John said. "Look, there's a pitcher plant." He pointed to a mottled green thing in a swampy area. "It eats bugs. See how the insides of the pitcher are lined with little hairs pointing downward? Bugs can go down but can't come up."

Jim learned the difference between the orange partridge berries and the scarlet berries of wintergreen and chewed some of the latter's leaves. They picked a few hazel nuts and got their fingers full of prickers as they peeled them, cracked them on a rock, and tasted the delicious little kernels. "I've got two quarts of them at home for winter eating," John said. "We put them in a wet burlap bag and thresh them by pounding it on a rock." How fast the morning passed! Though their roles had been reversed, with John being the teacher, Jim had loved every moment and was anxious to learn more. Now he was not so utterly alone; he had a real friend and a warm home. Tioga wasn't so bad, after all.

He also felt that way after their dinner. "Maijuka," they called the venison stew with turnips, potatoes and other vegetables in it. Mrs. Salmi said it was her last can of deer meat, but she knew John would shoot another buck in November as he had last year. An eight pointer, it was, and very tender. John was very proud. "Yah, just one shot," he said. "Got him after school in the Buckeye swamp. I'll take you there some time."

After the meal was finished Mrs. Salmi asked John to dig the rest of the carrots and turnips, put them in the sand boxes and take them to the cellar. Jim helped him cut off the tops then hold them upright as the sand was poured around them. The cellar was an interesting place lit dimly by small window wells. Shelves hanging from the ceiling were loaded with hundreds of jars of fruit. Five burlap bags of potatoes, a barrel of apples and a box of upended cabbages sat on the dirt floor. In one corner was a bench holding crocks of pickles and some large bowls of milk covered with cheesecloth. Jim asked why the jars were on the hanging shelves.

John grinned. "We have to keep them high," he said, "because at spring breakup a lot of water comes into the cellar. One year it was up to the sixth step. By that time though we've eaten all the vegetables. We can put these on the floor for now."

Then John took Jim out to help him fire up the sauna. A tight log structure, it belonged to the Salmis and to the Laitalas next door and the two families alternated heating it each week. "We go sauna in afternoon and the Laitalas after supper," he explained as he cautiously opened the door and looked in. "Sometimes there's a big black pine snake comes in the fall. I didn't want to scare you. They're harmless. No poisonous snakes in the U.P." It was dark in the first room, the dressing and cooling room, despite some light from a small window. Two benches sat along opposite walls, one bearing a farm kerosene lantern. A large wooden water barrel was in the center of the room. "Here's where we get undressed and wash before we go into the steam room," John said, "and where we cool off and dry ourselves later. The cracks in the floor let the water out."

Opening the door into the inner room, John saw a long boxstove covered with round rocks, another water barrel, the hot water one connected to the stove, and a set of steps or benches, one above the other. "Here's where we sit," John explained. "Once we've got the rocks heated good we pour dippers of water onto the rocks, and that makes the steam. The higher up you sit on the benches, the hotter it gets. You'll like it once you get used to it. Sure cleans out your pores, right to the bones."

After John opened a vent to help the fire get started and washed the room's only window, the two of them filled the water barrels by carrying pails of water from a well outside. Then they put some birchbark and a lot of pine wood in the stove and lit it. "We'll have to fire up again about two o'clock and that should have the rocks hot enough to cook us good." Knowing that Jim was dubious about the whole thing, John was enjoying himself. He pointed to a pile of cedar switches. "We use those to beat ourselves after we've been broiled," he said. "Too bad we don't have any snow yet. In winter sometimes we roll in it and then go sauna again and again. You'll sure get clean." Remembering the sponge baths he'd been taking in Aunt Lizzie's claw-footed bathtub with only two teakettles of water, Jim knew he needed such a cleaning, but he was apprehensive.

On their way back to the house Jim saw a very pretty girl brushing her yellow hair on the steps of the neighbor's house. "Who's that?" he asked.

"That's Ruth Keski," replied John. "You know her. She's the seventh grade teacher. She rooms and boards with the Laitalas. She's a Finn too." Jim went over and his shocked surprise made the girl giggle.

"Yes, it's me, Jim. You've caught me without my disguise. I don't need to wear those horrible glasses or keep my hair in a bun and am about to quit doing so." She went on to explain that when she'd started applying for teaching positions she'd been turned down three times because of her picture. "They said I looked too young to teach for them," she said. "So I bought these glasses and fixed my hair and had another picture taken, and Mr. Aronson wrote back offering me the Tioga job right away. Well, I thought I'd might as well keep looking that way at first because seventh graders need a stern looking teacher..."

Jim interrupted. "I can't believe it!" he said. "Will you take me to the Finnish church tomorrow?" She laughted at the implication but said she was glad they were neighbors. "No, I won't go to church but I'll walk to school with you Monday. I bet I'll shock my pupils too."

About four-thirty Mrs. Salmi took her sauna and then her "poikas" had their turn. Even the cooling room was steamy as they soaped and scrubbed and poured pails of very cold water over their heads. When Jim reached for his towel, John said no, that they should go in wet so the heat wouldn't be so bad at first. "You sit on the bottom bench. It's not so hot." he said.

When he opened the inner door, Jim felt as though he were in a blast furnace. The heat was incredible, overwhelming, and only his pride kept him from bolting. When John poured some dippers of hot water on the rocks a cloud of more steam filled the room. Jim sat down on the furthest corner of the lower bench only to spring up with a yell. "Oh, I forgot to tell you," John laughed. "Always sit in the middle of the bench. The hot nails are on the ends." Jim felt the sweat oozing out from every inch of his body but it didn't cool him a bit. How could John stand it up on the highest bench? It was hard to breathe and Jim could feel his heart pounding. He looked at his legs. They were beet red; even the soles of his feet were. His fingers dripped. He gasped for air. His eyes watered. But somehow he endured until John felt he'd had enough and led the way back to the cooling room. It seemed frigid there but his body didn't. As he stood there naked, a delicious tingling swept over him. Pins and needles even in his armpits. Oh what a relief and also what a wonderful sense of well-being and complete cleanliness! He felt loose all over as he dried himself with the towel and put on his clean clothing. When John went back inside for another broiling Jim was almost tempted to join him. "No, that's enough for the first time," he said to himself. "It wasn't really as bad as I'd expected. The hell it wasn't!"

That evening when Jim went up to his room to study, Mrs. Salmi soon came to get him. "No, Yimmy," she protested. "Bedroom for sleeping only. This your house too. You come down now. You read in living room if we bother you in kitchen." What a change from Aunt Lizzie's house! Most of his evenings thereafter were spent in the large kitchen at the round table or occasionally in the living room beside it. Mrs. Salmi had her loom there and often wove some of the rag rugs she made for sale as he was reading. Occasionally, when the thump, thump of the loom stopped for a moment to let her adjust a spindle, the two of them would have good conversation.

Aiti wanted to know all about college. She and her absent husband had saved for years so that their children could attend one. Neither of her other sons had been interested but Yonny was. Did Jim think Yonny was bright enough to go? How much would it cost to go to a university to be a teacher or doctor or scientist? What courses would he study? How long would it take? Jim told her he was sure John could handle it, that he was one of the brightest students in the whole high school. When Jim described scholarships and part-time jobs, and all the possibilities that opened up when one had a higher education, she hung on every word he said.

"We Finns from old country, we know education is good," Aiti responded. "In Finland only rich people send kids to school. My husband, he now tired of diamond drilling and being away so long, so far away. Maybe this be last year on the road for him then, but if Yonny need more raha, he go again."

One other evening she explored Jim's name. "Heiken? That almost Finn name. Where your family come from?"

Jim told her that it might have been Sweden, that his father had traced their ancestry back to an ancestor who had come from Sweden in a sailing ship to his country before the Revolutionary War, to what was then called New Sweden on the banks of the Delaware River.

"Heiken no Swede name," she protested, "but lots of Heikinens in old country. One family of Heikinens here in Tioga." When Jim remembered that his father had said the name had been shortened shortly after the first Heiken came, that perhaps Heiken came from Heikenson, Aiti was certain he was a Finn. "No, Heikenson not Swede name. You were Heikinen. Back then Sweden and Finland same country. Lots of Finns work in Sweden too. You Finlander, Yimmy." From that time on, when visitors came for coffee, she always introduced Jim as Mr. Heikinen. He didn't mind a bit. Indeed he felt honored. The Finns were fine people and perhaps he really had been one once. Anyway, he sure was enjoying the saunas now.

That whole fall season was a delight. Not just the teaching but the long hikes in the woods with Yonny as they hunted partridge and rabbits or ducks. Always there was something new to learn, and when they returned to that warm loving house Jim almost pinched himself, hardly being able to believe his good fortune.

Living in that Finn house was quite an experience. Many of the foods were completely strange to Jim but they were always good. For breakfast they often had kropsu, an oven-baked pancake, with maple syrup, and pulla, a delightful coffeecake. Sometimes dinner consisted of suola-silli, salted herring, with potatoes, and a fruit soup called hedelma. Always there was leipa, homemade bread, or occasionally nakki-leipa, hardtack, with newly churned butter on it. Jim even developed a taste for kirnu-piima, buttermilk, and drank that instead of coffee as he ate uuni-juusto, a baked soft cheese that looked like custard pie. It was no wonder that the first Finnish work he learned was kituksia, for "thank you."

As the days grew shorter and the evenings longer, there always seemed to be something interesting to do even when they sat in the kitchen. When he found that John could always beat him playing checkers, Jim sent home for his chess set and because he didn't want him to be discouraged, he occasionally invited Ruth over to learn the moves so she and John could play together. Both of them learned swiftly and soon were challenging him too. Aiti sat smilingly beside the kitchen range knitting or mending or winding a ball of rags she had cut and sewed for her loom.

One night after Jim had walked Ruth back to her house and had tried to kiss her but found she sure could dodge, aiti said to him, "I think you like Ruth, eh Yimmy? She make you good Finn wife and give many children. Why you no ask her sometime?" When he told her that Ruth didn't seem interested, she replied. "Not so, Yimmy. She beginning love for you. Women always know." Well, that was encouraging, but why did Ruth always shake his hand loose when he just tried to hold it as they walked home from school. And why, when they had been looking at the stars through a telescope he'd built from some lenses he'd found in the physics lab and he'd put his arm around her, she'd pulled away. Always she said "Not yet, Yimmy." "Not yet?" Damn her hide! Always "not yet."

Nevertheless, Ruth did seem to enjoy being with him, and once when Aiti had been ironing his shirts (she refused to take any money for doing them), Ruth had taken the iron from her and learned how to do it. And when the snows came Ruth would ski with him down Company Field to Lake Tioga and, by a little coffee fire, sit very close, closer than she needed to. There was also that stormy morning when the two of them encountered a huge drift on the way to school and he picked her up in his arms to help her through it. For just a moment he'd felt her relax and even snuggle up to him, but again when he tried to kiss her she dodged and all he got was a mouth of wet parka. "Not yet," she said again and when she laughed outrageously he threw her into a snowbank.

Ruth also, unlike most of the teachers, attended all the basketball home games that Jim coached, usually coming with John's mother, John being the star of the team. Basketball, Tioga's only organized sport, always brought big and enthusiastic crowds, perhaps because there was nothing else to do in wintertime, or because it only cost a dime admission. To his surprise Jim found his players still using both hands to shoot baskets. They'd squat with legs apart and swing the ball up from between them before throwing it in a high looping arc. Jim taught them the one-handed way of shooting he'd learned in Chicago. "Don't arch it; just get it over the front rim," he had to tell them again and again. The training paid off. They won most of their games, even the two with Michigamme. Strangers shook Jim's hand when they met him on the street. "You-sta goot coach, I tink! You come back next year too?" Yes, coaching was fun.

Just before Christmas when he was to return to his home in Chicago, Jim prowled Flynn's store hunting for presents for his aiti and Ruth but could find nothing, so he took the train for Ishpeming one Saturday, returning with a large box of Whitman's sampler candies and a dozen roses double-wrapped against the cold. He'd planned to give the chocolates to Ruth and the roses to Aiti, but when he remembered his aiti's love of sweets he gave the candy to her with half of the roses and brought the other six roses to Ruth. Both were overcome by the gifts. Aiti even wept and hugged him. Ruth didn't, but for the first time she touched his cheek affectionately as she told him how much she appreciated the present. Somehow the Christmas vacation at home seemed very long and Jim was glad to get back to Tioga.

When Valentine's Day came, Jim again brought them flowers from the Ishpeming greenhouse, and in return received a batch of his favorite saffron raisin buns from Aiti and a homemade valentine from Ruth which said: "Roses are red and violets are blue; Tioga was made for just us two." Not much love in it but he put it under his pillow that night.

Finally spring came with its usual breakup mess. Jim and Ruth couldn't walk in the woods because there was still too much wet snow, and except for the hill street all the roads were quagmires of mud. He felt the old hunger to walk and walk that all in the U.P. know at that time of year, so one Sunday afternoon he and Ruth went along the railroad track toward Red Bridge to see the river bursting its icy bonds. Unfortunately, some damned little French kids followed them for a while, chanting "Take down yer pants and give him a chance." Seeing his fury, Ruth told him just to ignore them and soon they were left behind. Oh, it was a glorious U.P. day - sunshine and warm with a few lazy white clouds drifting over a sky as blue as her eyes. Near a rock cut, they found a patch of arbutus already in bloom. Ruth lay down in it to smell the wonderful fragrance and Jim did so too, right beside her, their faces separated by only a few of the vines. Suddenly he tried again to kiss her but got just a taste of her blonde hair. "Not yet, Yimmy!" she said in a whisper. "Not yet!"

"Damn your 'not yets' " he yelled, pulling her up by the shoulders and shaking her till her hair swirled. "What the hell is wrong with you? It's spring! Spring! You drive me crazy. Haven't you got anything but icewater inside your skin?" He put her down and covered his face with his hands. They walked home without speaking to each other.

The next morning Jim walked to school early and alone, and also that afternoon he came home alone. He would put Ruth out of his mind. To hell with her! There were other girls! It would be misery being married to such a cold fish anyway. But, despite his wishes, he couldn't help thinking of her. Day and night he held her in his arms but only in his thoughts. Only once, when John took him trout fishing in the rapids, was he able to forget her. It became clear to him that he'd just have to get out of Tioga. So when Mr. Aronson offered him a contract for the following year, Jim replied that he wasn't sure he'd return but would give him his answer before the end of school.

Aiti became concerned with the change that had come over Jim. "You sick, Yimmy?" she asked when he ate only half of one of her delicious pasties. "You no happy any more. What wrong?" He couldn't tell her then but later one evening when they were together in the living room, he studying and she working her loom, he blurted out the whole story. Ruth was driving him nuts, he said. He was much in love with her but she wouldn't respond. She wouldn't even let him kiss her. He would have to go away so he could forget her. He probably wouldn't be back in Tioga next year.

"You want marry her?" Aiti asked gently. When he nodded miserably she smiled. "You don't know Finn girls, good Finn girls, I guess. They save it! Why you no ask her to marry her and see?"

So one late evening in May when Jim saw Ruth going to the sauna clad in a kimono and bath towel, he waited a bit then went too. Quietly opening the outer door to the dressing room, he disrobed and hung his clothing over hers, then entered the steam room. Ruth was sitting on the lower bench, naked and beautiful as the dawn, and she squealed when she saw him. "No! No!" she screamed. "No! Not yet! Get out of here!" But when he put his arm around her there in the steam and drew her close and asked her to marry him she flung her bare arms around his neck and kissed him passionately. "Oh Yimmy, why you no ask before?"

ONE DAY IN MAY, 1915

4:30 A.M. I was a-wakened by an angry snarl at my bedroom window. It was Puuko, our black tomcat, back from a long night of fornication. Because it was the middle of May and the mosquitoes and black flies had not yet arrived, I'd opened that window six inches when I went to bed so I wouldn't have to get up at dawn to let the old devil in. It was not sufficient because Puuko wouldn't stoop for man or beast. He was too proud. After all, what other tomcat had been able to change the color of all Tioga's cats from grey to black in his nine lifetimes? Groaning, I staggered over to lift the window sash, then went back to my blankets.

5:00 A.M. Louie Fachon made himself some coffee and after eating six blueberry pancakes went down to the creek to get the pail of chub minnows he'd stashed there. The big pike in Lake Tioga always bit best shortly after dawn. It was going to be a fine U.P. day, he thought. Perhaps too good.

5:30 A.M. Pierre Rousseau our Prophet, measured the level of the water in his well and examined his weather stick. "Oui," he said, "Ze weathair, she's goin' be fine zis day for sure." Never had he seen the water drop so much in one night. Never had he seen the weather stick point so high.

6:00 A.M. Wakened by the roosters, all the dogs in Tioga rose from their beds, stretched, and began to howl as the sun came up. No, not all of them. Old Pullo, the spotted hound, was sleeping outside the fence at Aunt Lizzie's house waiting for her to bring out Lulubelle to do her duty and dirty. When she and the Pekinese appeared, Pullo opened one eye and said a loud, "Galoom!"

By this time most of the chimneys in town wore plumes of white smoke rising straight up into the windless air, as our people made their breakfast fires. Cows mooed, insisting on being milked. The morning freight train's time whistle filled the surrounding hills with echoes. Time to get up!

7:00 A.M. Pierre Paquin limped up the long stairs to the Catholic church and ejected his cud of Redman tobacco before pulling on the bell rope that rang the Angeles. All of us in town, even the Finns, loved the sweet sound of those morning bells.

Passing through our kitchen with the rich smell of new coffee, my father greeted the fine spring day by blowing his nose as he stood on the back steps. A mighty snort to which our neighbors set their watches, it was his daily ritual. No handkerchiefs either. Dad always said that a rich man put in his pocket what a poor man threw away.

Robins bounced across the lush green lawn with their hands in their pockets, seeking a worm too lazy to have crawled back in its hole. Crows cawed in the Grove. In a hundred houses wives turned pancakes that would soon be smothered with the maple syrup boiled down just a month before. Charley Olafson unlocked the jail cage in the Town Hall to let Pete Ramos out. Making his rounds at midnight, he'd found Pete drunk and unconscious lying on the sidewalk in front of the school. Neither of the men said a word. It had happened before and would happen again.

Mrs. Hokkinen went out to her strawberry patch to enjoy the early morning sunshine and to see how the plants had made it through the winter. They looked fine. They should have! All through March she'd emptied the slop jar on them because she never knew when her husband might shoot up their outhouse.

7:30 A.M. Mrs. Waisanen who was then doing our milking, brought in a ten-quart pail of warm milk and I hastened to feed Rosie, our Jersey cow. That milk would be put into large brown bowls in the cellar so the thick yellow cream would rise to the top for skimming. Tomorrow, Saturday, was butter churning day. I also let our white horse, Billy, out into the barnyard so he could roll around a bit while I fed the chickens. Then I began pumping water up into the tank upstairs. Three hundred strokes later, mother stopped me though I knew the tank was far from being filled. "Cully," she said. "It's getting late and you'll be tardy for school. Better get going. You can finish your pumping when you come home for dinner."

135

8:00 A.M. Mr. Marchand drives his old horse, Maude, up our hill street, bringing the mail. Annie, our postmistress, had to read all the postcards first, but soon had it distributed in the boxes as four or five women and men waited in the anteroom in front of the partition. Not Scotty McGee. He only came to the post office once a month to get his pension check from the Oliver Mining Company. Having had his coffee and hardtack, Mr. McGee was reading the bible to his dog, Tam O'Shanter. Down in the valley, Sieur La Tour, the oldest man in the village, was sitting on his front stoop in the sunshine, remembering the days when Tioga was only a stage coach stop on the road to Fort Wilkins at the tip of the Keweenaw Peninsula. Also in the valley, Josette Bourdon was filling the big copper boiler on the kitchen range so her mother could wash the clothing the trainmen brought over, but she was happy that she would not have to do the ironing now that she was clerking at Flynn's store uptown.

9:00 A.M. Aunt Lizzie removes her wig from the teakettle that has been warming it, gets dressed and starts her daily gossip rounds. Lenna Kangas starts her spring cleaning by scrubbing the floor of her summer kitchen, glad that the old potbellied stove her husband had put outside to heat all outdoors was gone. Leif Larsen goes to Beaverdam Swamp to get cedars to support his perfect outhouse so the kids couldn't overturn it, come Halloween. My father reluctantly hitches Billy, our white horse, to the buckboard, wishing that the roads weren't still in so much of a mess. He preferred making his calls in the new 1914 Ford but the roads were too bad. He also dreaded having to give Old Lady Haitema an enema again, trying to get hold of that tapeworm of hers that had broken off last time.

9:30 A.M. It was sure hard to be in school that fine spring day. Our teacher, P.P. Polson seemed ornrier than ever, so we kids raised hell when her kidneys got the best of her and she had to leave the room for a few minutes. I plugged the peephole in the classroom door with some gum I'd been chewing furtively all morning, and when we saw that bony finger pop it open all of us were studying hard when she entered. Unfortunately, Mule Cardinal couldn't control himself and burst out laughing so all of us did too. But we stopped abruptly when Miss Polson lifted Mule out of his seat by his ears and stood him in the corner until recess.

10:00 A.M. Smoking Peerless in their corncob pipes, Eino and Emil began to play their first checker game of the day, but they got to arguing so hard about when to plant their peas and beets they forgot whose turn it was to move. In the living room of our house Grandma Van got out her knitting, thinking perhaps that those long needles would sure be good for goosing anyone who passed by her. In our kitchen Mother was baking Dad a mince pie. Uptown, old Bridget Murphy shooed the chickens off her bedposts and Paddy, her pig, out of the house and into his pen, fearing that Father Hassel might be coming up to examine her soul. Josette's mother hung the trainmen's clothes on the line as the midmorning freight chugged past the depot. A good day for drying even if there wasn't much of a breeze.

11:00 A.M. Jacques Cousteau, his wife Marie, and Willie the springer spaniel, all sitting high on the seat of their hay wagon, drove to Flynn's store singing old French songs all the way up the hill. It was spring! He would buy Marie a pretty new hat, maybe with pink ribbons on it, and buy himself a whole pail of Peerless tobacco so he'd feel rich. Higley swept out his saloon, then had to mop it too. "Why don't them bastards use the spittoon?" he asked himself for the thousandth time. Untu Heikkala sanded the share (the blade) of his one-horse plow until it shone, then tested the soil of his garden by kicking a few holes in it. No, he decided, the ground was still too wet to plow the potato patch.

Noon. At his little cabin by Mud Lake, our old hermit Eric Niemi, began to fry some salt pork in the cast-iron frying pan. No potatoes; they'd gone soft. Just a mess of sprouts. It would be trout and hardtack. Enough! He'd caught five small trout in the creek that morning, so he squeezed each one till it squeaked, put them in the pan and when they were brown he gnawed them like sweet corn, heads, tails, bones and all. Very good!

Mother had a fine dinner ready for us: pot roast and mashed potatoes. Dad served me the part with the marrow-filled bone because he knew I liked that marrow with salted crackers. My little brother Joe got part of it, not that he liked marrow as I did, but just because he couldn't bear to have me have something he didn't, the wart! After Dad had his second piece of venison mincemeat pie, he patted his vest and said to mother, "A fine meal, Madam. You have acquired merit!" Then he told us of his morning calls. "Edyth, I think I've finally found a way to convince the Finns that they shouldn't eat raw fish. I got that tapeworm out of Mrs. Haitema this morning, all eight yards of it. Brought it out of her hind end, hand over hand, like hauling in a big pike. Lord, how she squealed! I'm going to put it in a big bottle with formaldehyde and show it to any Finn I think is eating the stuff." "Oh John," Mother interrupted. "Don't tell those awful tales at dinner time, please!"

1:00 P.M. Herb Anderson, the one we called the Deacon, drove up the hill in his buggy and tied his horse to the hitching post in front of my father's hospital. "Doc," he said, "I want to buy some potassium permanganate if you got some." When Dad asked him why, he said, "Got an old horse I aim to trade one of these days. Trouble is Betsey's nigh to being seventeen years old now and shows it. Getting pretty gray, she is. I've filed her teeth but I got to get some color on her mane and hide."

"But potassium permanganate will turn her purple," my father protested. "That won't do you any good."

"Oh, I don't use it straight, Doc. I mix a spoon of it with strong hot coffee and that turns it brown. A trick my pappy taught me. Makes the brown stain indelible. Nothing'll wash it off a horse's hide."

Mrs. Bourdon takes the clothes off the line and sets up the ironing board with a sigh. Wetting her finger, she touches the bottom of one of the sad irons on the range and hears the hiss. Hot enough! She'll still be ironing until six when Josette comes home from the store.

2:00 P.M. Jules Fontaine and Matti Mattila, pumping the handcar as fast as they could to reach the side track at Clowry Siding before the afternoon freight train tore down on them, managed to do so just in time. "Jules," said Matti to his old friend, "I hear you're going to run for Township Treasurer. How'd you feel if I run too?"

Jim Fortas, Tioga's inveterate gambler and Laf Bodine, our best poacher, were sitting on a baggage cart outside the depot. They'd heard that the D.S.S. & A might be hiring temporary help to fix the red bridge over the Escanaba, but the station agent had not returned from his noon break. Meanwhile, they were watching a black and tan hound walking toward them. "Laf," said Jim, "Betcha a dollar that there hound will turn around three times before he lies down." "What odds you give me?" asked Laf. "My buck against your two bits though you're stealing me blind," said Jim although he'd watched that hound before and he knew it always turned around three times before it lay down. "OK!" But this time the hound only turned around twice.

3:00 P.M. Mrs. Saari went across the road to Mrs. Pekkari's house for afternoon coffee and they discussed their mate's competence in bed among other things.

Down at the blacksmith shop Paddy Feeney has an hour free time although Pete Himmel will be bringing over his team to be shod later. Knowing that soon school will be let out and the kids will come to watch him, Paddy heats up the forge and makes a puzzle for them out of iron, consisting of a heart, a ring, and a chain. They'd have fun trying to get the heart off the ring. Not too hard! One of them would be able to do it.

Siiri Sivola builds a fire in their sauna. John will be needing one after his long day in the woods. They would be taking the train to Ishpeming in the morning to buy her a new dress and him some axe handles and a new pitchfork.

43:30 P.M. Old Blue Balls, our tough school superintendent, catches Mullu and Toivo fighting in the schoolyard, a no no. He hauls them up to his office but feeling a bit mellow because he and my father would be going trout fishing up the West Branch next morning, he just gives Mullu *The Strap* and tells him to wallop Toivo ten times, with Toivo getting his turn later. Unfortunately, Mullu didn't hit hard enough so Old Blue Balls had to show him how to do it right. Both kids were bawling when they left.

4:00 P.M. Mrs. Hivonen goes to see Ben Tremblay, Tioga's wise man. She explains that Lempi, her teen-aged daughter is pregnant but will not tell who the father was. Ben gave the matter some thought, then said, "When the egg is laid, to hell with the rooster." And that was that!

Father Hassel, our old Catholic priest, comes to our house for his weekly chess game with my father and for the glass of whiskey and cigar that always went with it. "How's the sinning going in Tioga, Father?" my Dad asked. The priest chuckled. "It's spring, Doctor," he replied. "You'll have your answer nine months from now."

Fisheye and I get some redworms out of the manure pile and go down to Beaverdam Creek. He caught a seven-inch trout but all I caught was a big redhorse sucker which I took home for Peter White, our big pig. Peter sure liked those suckers. How he squealed!

5:00 P.M. Tim O'Leary brings Molly Malone a big bunch of wild iris (blue flags, we called them) only to have her fling them in his Irish face. That wooing was sure going hard.

The cows began coming back for the evening milking, mooing lustily as they swung their big bags from side to side climbing the hill street. I let Rosy into our barnyard and got a pail of hot bran and water to put in her stall. Billy got a big pail of oats and some fresh hay from the loft. And a sugar lump!

Madam Olga, our fortuneteller, grateful for Fisheye's replenishing her woodbox, reads his palm and tells him he'll have nine children when he grows up.

6:00 P.M. Mr. Marchand brings up the evening mail. It is late because of some accident or something down the line that delayed the South Shore train. Annie, the postmistress, puts up a note on the door saying, "Having my supper. Mail will be disturbed from 7 to 8 due to late delivery."

Sylvie, Father Hassel's ugly housekeeper, burns his evening pot roast. That takes some doing but the priest forgives her, of course.

7:00 P.M. Mr. Rich, having had his supper, unlocks the front door to his combination barber shop and poolroom. Three of our men enter. It's a place to go and only costs ten cents a game per player. On a good night Mr. Rich will take in two dollars from the pool table and perhaps another half dollar in haircuts at a quarter each. Not much, but it's a living and for an ex-miner with a wooden leg it's helped him make do. As two of the men rack up their balls and chalk their cues, a stranger enters, evidently a lumberjack with a very heavy beard and shaggy hair. "Just come from Silverthorne's camp," he explained. "They kept me on after the log drive to build their new cook shanty. Haven't been out of the woods since last summer. How much you charge to get rid of this hair and beard?" Mr. Rich looked him over, then said, "Fifty cents, maybe seventy-five. There's a lot of cutting and shaving to do." "OK," said the jack and climbed up into the red plush barber chair. Mr. Rich didn't put the apron around him. Just parted his hair and looked. "No sir!" he said. "No sir! You're lousy, lousy, Mister. I wouldn't cut your hair for ten dollars. Come back when you're free of the critters." As the lumberjack left, the man who wasn't playing pool said, "Don't blame you a bit, Mr. Rich. Don't blame you a bit! Lots of them lumber camps are full of lice. Worst one I seen was A.W. Read's Camp Five on the Yellow Dog. They damn near ate us to the bone. We had a young fella there just starting out and he like to go crazy, he did. Not used to it like us old-timers. We tells the kid to go ask the cook for a lot of salt and rub it in everywhere he got hair, crotch and all. 'What good would that do?' asks the greenhorn and we tells him that after he's got hisself salted down good and plenty, to go down to the creek and soak his bare feet in it, that then the lice, thirsty after eating all that salt meat, would go to his feet and be washed off by the current. Damned if the young fool didn't do it. Gadamighty how we laughed!"

The bells of the Catholic Church tolled Vespers.

Old Billy Bones pulled his little red wagon down to the depot. All of us knew that under the burlap bags that covered it were jugs of Billy Bones' extra-powerful dandelion wine to be sold to the trainmen. Three or four kids had picked bunches of arbutus that they would peddle to the passengers of the evening train from the Copper Country, if they could sneak onto the coaches without the conductor seeing them.

8:00 P.M. Some of the little kids are playing hide-and-seek; others knock-the-stick; still older ones are playing shinny, knocking a condensed milk can from one goal to another with the crooked sticks they'd gotten from the swamp. Swallows circled the tall chimney of the abandoned mine and every so often a few would plummet down into it for their night nesting. Horses clomped up the wooden sidewalk leaving piles of golden nuggets behind them.

8:30 P.M. The sun went down at the far shore of Lake Tioga tinting the water pink and gold. Men who'd been fishing off the railroad bridge for the pike and walleyes that were making their spawning run up the river picked up their minnow buckets and started the long walk home. At the depot, Maggie O'Conner, the station's cleaning woman, cleaned the spittoon and practiced a bit of spitting herself. In the back room of Callahan's store, Dinny played a hand of solitaire, wishing it were Saturday night when he and the other Regulars of the Last Man Under The Table Club would tap a new keg of beer and play poker.

9:00 P.M. Dad tells me I don't have to go to bed yet, that he wants me to pick a can of nightcrawlers so he and Mr. Donegal can fish for trout on the West Branch. I get the flashlight and look but they aren't out yet. "That's all right," Dad said. "Just hang around until they do appear." Whoops!

At Higley's saloon things aren't jumping yet but most of the usual customers are there. Pete Halfshoes sits in the corner of his booth nursing his second beer and saying nothing. He will have just one more before climbing the hill to his house where Mabel, his pet skunk and bed partner, waits for him. Laf Bodine is telling again how he outwitted the game warden by wearing his snowshoes backwards. Slimber Vester starts a long rambling lie about how he wrestled a big buck and broke its neck. Arvo Mattson began to tell his bear story. "No you don't!" yelled Higley. "The last damn time you told that story about climbing the tree to get away from that bear, you grabbed my chandelier and crashed it to the floor." "Yah," said Arvo. "Rotten branch!"

The Trevarthen boys and their father parted the swinging doors of the saloon and got an enthusiastic welcome. Twirling his black mustache, Higley was happy to see them too. "All the beer you want for as long as you sing them old songs," he said, sliding three mugs down the polished bar. "But start with 'Turaluralura' that Irish lullaby one." The Trevarthens obliged in close harmony and even Higley had a tear in his left eye. "Nuts to that Irish stuff," yelled someone. "Give us 'A Hot Time in the Old Town Tonight' ". Things were finally getting going in Higley's saloon.

10:00 P.M. One by one the kerosene lamps in the village flickered out and the yellow windows turned black. I bring in the full can of worms and let Puuko out to do his duty. As Grampa Gage used to say "England expects every man to do his duty; so does Puuko!" Those French cats down in the valley will squall tonight. After the Trevarthens sing their way up the hill under the tall maples overhanging the sidewalk, it is very quiet in Tioga.

Except in the Jensen house where Alf snores so loudly Helga has to put more cotton in her ears.

141

POSTSCRIPT

I cannot end this book without expressing my appreciation to the many readers who have written me. Through them I have made many new friends. That's really something at the age of eighty-three when most of my old friends have passed away. The letters have come from all over, even one from Hong Kong, and from people of all ages and walks of life. A nine-year-old boy wants me to be his grampa; a teenaged girl stranded in Wisconsin writes that she can't wait to grow up so she can go back to the U.P. again; an old man thanks me for reviving memories of his own youth. All of them tell me that they share my love for that still wild country above the Straits.

I'm sure that this mail is what has kept me telling the stories of the interesting people I knew as a boy early in this century. I've tried to quit several times fearing that there may be dotage in my anecdotage, but then I get some more mail telling the tales their grandparents told them about the old days, or providing glimpses of their own lives. The fact that I can still have some impact, can make some unknown reader chuckle or share a tear with me, enriches an old man's life, so again I thank you, my friends.

Most of those letters are short but a few of them are not. I can't resist including two of the latter.

The first comes from Amy Van Ooyinen of Ironwood and describes how the people at the far end of the U.P. make the best of the long winter:

"Saima Walkonen phoned. The Grandmothers Ski Marathon would be held tomorrow at eleven. Her husband, Whitey, had made the trails through their property and put up some of his crazy signs along them. There would be six or seven grandmas curing their cabin fever.

"Lena went with me and we were the second to arrive because Sylvia Niemi was ahead of us, dressed in very classy tight stretch pants like those the pro skiers wear. She must be nearing seventy-five but isn't telling. Lena wore a man's quilted overalls with a heavy down vest. Saima's three sisters then came and we made a nice row of sliding women in front of Whitey's woodshed. That woodshed is a very patriotic one because Whitey has painted an American flag on it. Next to the flag, however, is fastened an open #3 trap with its trigger pan painted red and above that is written 'To Register Complaints, Press Here!' Standing beside another sign he had just painted, Whitey saw us off. That sign said, 'Never mind the dog. Beware of the Husband!'

"So we shoved off in single file. As we entered the woods, there was another sign: 'Alpha and Omega'. Lena bumped into me. 'My skis are too slippery,' she explained. I told her to go ahead, that she was faster than I was. Besides, if she'd fallen on me in that three feet of snow, I would have been buried till spring.

"Suddenly we saw what looked like a black bear half rising out of the snow, but it was evident that he'd already eaten because all that was left was an old red cap. Whitey had sure been busy preparing for us. A bit further along the trail was posted the warning, 'Beware of Snow Snakes'. After that a grove of maple saplings waist-high in snow had to be conquered. Then around a bend was a sign saying 'Head Hunters in the Woods' with a spear bearing a doll's head on top of it. On we strode.

"But Whitey had been thoughtful of the seven grandmothers. There beside the trail was a comfort station. No outhouse, just an old metal door hung between two trees and a log to sit on. Though the Sears Roebuck catalog was a bit wet, the door was clearly labeled 'VE SA' in large letters, the Finnish word for outhouse. Beside it in smaller letters were directions. 'We aim to please you. You aim too!' 'Radioactive Heap. Pull chain; Wash hands!'

"Much comforted, we entered a less well traveled trail with difficult gullies and hills to tackle, but we weren't lost. We found a sign and arrow that pointed north to Helsinki, Finland, only 4853 miles and one-fourth foot. When the trail went up a long hill we were getting tired. I noticed Marion leaning heavily forward on her skis, not a good position because the heaviest part of a lady comes last and so she slid backwards. There was a sign saying, 'The worst day of skiing is better than the best day of working.' Marion looked at it and said, 'Oh Shut Up!'

"Finally we came again to the section line of Whitey's property. 'All may trespass here' it said, 'If you have permission.' A bit further we found a kitchen fork fastened to a tree sign: 'Fork in the Road' and beyond that another sign saying 'Krik Krossing,' telling us also that the water in it ran to the Atlantic Ocean via Mud Creek, Montreal River, and Lakes Superior, Huron, Erie and Ontario. We were careful not to get swept away.

At long last we came to the Alpha and Omega sign again and then back to Saima's and Whitey's house. Potluck has waiting and did it ever taste good! Coffee, homemade bread, korpua, Spanish rice, two kinds of salad and spicy apple bars.

"Who won the Grandmother's Marathon? We all did."

Here's another. Charlie Shilling, its author, is a born storyteller and his accounts of his childhood on the farm have delighted me.

"When I was still at home we had a neighbor who had two boys a little older than me. Their Dad done blasting with dynamite, blasting stumps, drainage ditches, and stuff like that. Well, we kids became quite knowledgeable about things you could do with dynamite - like fishing. One day we were up on the hill playing in the woods back of our house and one of the boys had a stick of dynamite that he took when the old man wasn't looking. We were thinking of something we could blow up, when one of my Dad's old coon dogs come up where we were. Now that dog was a no-good old possum dog and hurting so bad Dad had talked about shooting him all fall and winter but he wasn't worth a shotgun shell. Well, we decided to do the job for Dad by tying that stick of dynamite to his tail and putting him out of his misery quick. We had no trouble catching him or tying on the dynamite with a long fuse that we lit. But that damn old dog wouldn't run away and keeps following us even when we throwed stones at him. So we did the running. Run home. We ran faster. So did that old hound. We ran up the back porch steps as the dog run under the porch. Well, in less time than it takes me to tell this we didn't have any back porch or steps. And we didn't have to dig a very big hole."

Dear Cully:

I was born in Champion (You called it Tioga), and your father delivered me. That was in 1899 and I grew up there until the mine closed when my folks moved to California. That was a good place to grow up, but I never made it back there. We lived downtown in a white-washed cabin on the road just north of the blacksmith shop. I picked spring beauties and adders tongues and bloodroot in the Grove behind your father's hospital. I climbed the steep hill often even in winter to go to school or to Mass. I slid on Sliding Rock too. Your books helped me to go back, after all.

Marie Rousseau

Dear Cully:

You write like it was when I was a boy. Write some more.

Kris Carlson

P.S. I keep your books in my outhouse and read a story every time.

Thank you again, all of you.

Cully Gage
3821 W. Milham
Portage, MI 49002

Grampa Cully once taught me never to set the hook too soon on a bass trying to swallow the minnow "or you'll both go away hungry. But don't wait too long or the bugger will swallow yer hook!"

He knows how to catch people too when he throws out a tantalizing tale. Like the one I swallowed which for years he played out to my folly. Then he hauled me in and cut the line quoting from the Mikado, "No, no lie that. It's merely corroborative detail intended to give artistic verisimilitude to a bald and unconvincing narrative."

With that I offer these illustrations as merely corroborative artistry to Cully's rich and convincing narrative.

Andrew Amor is a graduate of The University of Michigan. he practiced as an architect in Detroit for four years and is now in Tuscany, Italy, working as an aesthetic inspector of granite for five months, with his wife Elizabeth and 9-month-old son Peter.

We at Avery Color Studios thank you for purchasing this book. We hope it has provided many hours of enjoyable reading.

Learn more about Michigan and the Great Lakes area through a broad range of titles that cover mining and logging days, early Indians and their legends, Great Lakes shipwrecks, Cully Gage's Northwoods Readers (full of laughter and occasional sadness), and full-color pictorials of days gone by and the natural beauty of this land. Beautiful note stationery is also available.

For a free catalog, please call 800-722-9925 in Michigan or 906/226-3338, or tear out this page and mail it to us. Please tape or staple the card and put a stamp on it.

PLEASE RETURN TO:

Avery
COLOR STUDIOS

P.O. Box 308
Marquette MI 49855

CALL TOLL FREE
1-800-722-9925

Your complete shipping address:

_____

_____

_____

_____

Fold, Staple, Affix Stamp and Mail

_____

_____

_____

Avery
COLOR STUDIOS

P.O. Box 308
Marquette MI 49855